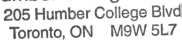
Table of CONTENTS

MINISTER'S Message

Iam pleased to present the 14th edition of *The State of Canada's Forests*. Canada is a recognized world leader in sustainable forest management and in developing innovative and practical approaches to addressing forest sector issues. Underlying this reputation is our ability to generate and apply new knowledge. This edition of The State of Canada's Forests focuses on the latest research on forest fires—an area that many Canadians may not necessarily associate with sustainable forest management.

In fact, outside the domain of forest experts, few people realize that fires are a natural and important process in the forest ecosystem—especially given the many evocative images and the level of media and public attention during last year's fire season. This year's report examines the complex issues surrounding forest fires so that Canadians may clearly understand their causes and effects, including the mitigation strategies and technologies that forest managers use.

The report also explores the human dimension of forest fires. The Points of View section presents how governments, local authorities and residents dealt with the forest fire that swept through Kelowna, British Columbia, last year.

In addition to the central theme of forest fires, the report presents the latest data and trends in traditional forest products as well as non-timber forest products and forest conditions. You will also find a synopsis of this year's major activities and accomplishments across the country and a new "For the Record" section that looks at the issues of genetically modified trees and clearcutting.

I am confident that Canadians will find the 2003–2004 edition of *The State of Canada's Forests* to be insightful and helpful in putting last year's fire season into perspective. Natural Resources Canada remains committed to conserving the integrity and diversity of our forests—and furthering the Government of Canada's commitment to building a sustainable economy for the 21st century, a healthier environment and strong communities, while affirming Canada's place in the world.

The Honourable R. John Efford
Minister of Natural Resources

1

Up
FRONT

An **OVERVIEW** of Canada's Forests

When Canadians think of their forests, it is often the recreation they can enjoy with their families and scenic views of trees and fresh water that come to mind. But forests also preserve the terrestrial ecological balance, support an $81.8-billion forest industry, and provide a myriad of wood products used in every household in Canada. The challenge for governments is to balance these competing interests with sustainable forest management approaches.

From an ecological standpoint, forests produce oxygen and remove carbon dioxide from the atmosphere, help to purify water and moderate climate, stabilize soil and regulate water flow. Canada's eight forest regions range from towering coastal rainforests in British Columbia to sparse and slow-growing forests at the Arctic tree line. Collectively, the regions are habitat to some 180 tree species.

The composition and age class structure of Canada's forests are determined through cycles of disturbances and renewal. Most of our forests grow in even-aged stands that evolve as a result of large-scale disturbances, such as fire or insect outbreaks. Each year, such outbreaks affect several million hectares of our forests.

Recently released statistics from Canada's Forest Inventory (CanFI 2001) tell us there are 401.5 million hectares of forest and other wooded land in Canada. The other wooded land makes up 23% of this area and includes treed wetland as well as land with slow-growing, scattered trees. Of the forest and other wooded land, the Crown owns 93%. The remainder is owned privately by some 425 000 land owners.

Eighty-seven percent is classified as stocked, or supporting tree growth. Of this forest, about a third has been assessed as young, another third as mature or overmature, and a final third as uneven-aged or unclassified. In terms of forest type, 66% of Canada's forests are softwoods, 22% are hardwoods, and 12% are mixedwoods.

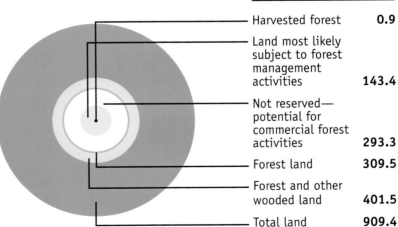

Canada's Forests
(million hectares)

Harvested forest	0.9
Land most likely subject to forest management activities	143.4
Not reserved— potential for commercial forest activities	293.3
Forest land	309.5
Forest and other wooded land	401.5
Total land	909.4

3

About Canada's FOREST INVENTORY (CanFI) 2001 Statistics

As a recognized world leader in sustainable forest management, Canada must be able to demonstrate to the world that its forest sector is economically viable, environmentally responsible and socially accountable. To reach this goal, we must develop and implement a complete, well-defined and accurate inventory of national forest land.

To meet the needs of forest managers and policy makers, the Canadian Forest Service compiles Canada's Forest Inventory (CanFI) by collecting data from provincial, territorial and other forest management inventories. CanFI statistics were compiled in 1981, 1986, 1991 and 2001.

CanFI 2001 is a compilation of existing inventories. Since CanFI 2001 differs from the previous inventory (CanFI 1991) in a number of ways, these data cannot be compared meaningfully. Definitions and methodologies have been changed, the inventory coverage has been extended to include all of Canada's land area, and more land cover classes are used to reflect a focus on the forest rather than on timber. Measurement methodology has also been changed, particularly in northern Canada. In 1991, forest area north of 60° was determined using maps generated in the early 1980s or before. CanFI 2001, on the other hand, uses a satellite interpretation, which improves our ability to differentiate forest from non-forest areas. As a result, some areas that were previously thought to be forest are, in fact, not forested. These differences mean that comparisons between the 1991 and 2001 CanFI inventories would be misleading.

But even beyond these differences, we need to make comparisons over time to answer questions about the sustainable development of Canada's forests. Therefore, a new approach to national forest inventory is needed, one that continually updates the picture of our forests and allows assessment of changes over time.

A new design, Canada's National Forest Inventory, has been developed and is being implemented in cooperation with the provinces and territories. This new design will replace the current CanFI approach and allow comparisons over time. The first statistical report using the new inventory is expected by 2006.

4

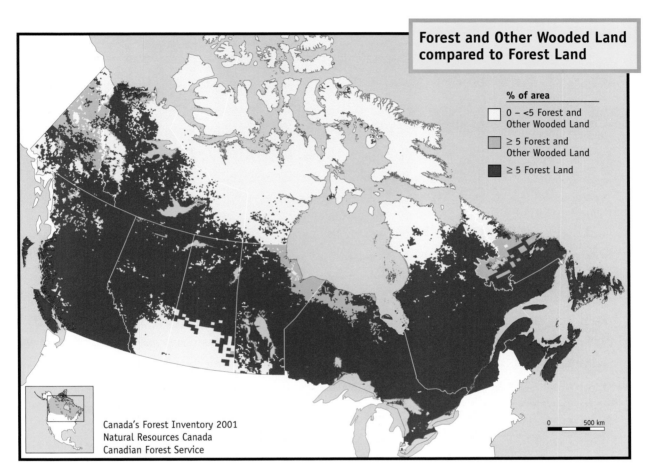

Forest and Other Wooded Land compared to Forest Land

% of area

☐ 0 – <5 Forest and Other Wooded Land

☐ ≥ 5 Forest and Other Wooded Land

■ ≥ 5 Forest Land

Canada's Forest Inventory 2001
Natural Resources Canada
Canadian Forest Service

0   500 km

Canada's FOREST FACTS for 2003-2004

- Canada is steward to about 10% OF THE WORLD'S FORESTS, 30% of the world's boreal forests, and 20% of the world's fresh water.

- There are about 400 MILLION HECTARES OF FOREST AND OTHER WOODED LAND. The 92 million hectares of other wooded land consists of treed wetland as well as slow-growing and scattered-treed land.

- Canada has 309.5 MILLION HECTARES OF FOREST LAND; of this, about 293 million hectares are not reserved and therefore potentially available for commercial forest activities.

- Of the 293 million hectares, about 143 million are considered accessible and most likely to be subject to FOREST MANAGEMENT ACTIVITIES.

- Of these 143 million, about 1 million hectares are HARVESTED annually.

- There were 8218 RECORDED FOREST FIRES in Canada in 2003 with approximately 1.6 million hectares of forested land burned, a reduction of 1.2 million hectares from the previous year.

- Canada's forests are the backbone of an $81.8-billion FOREST INDUSTRY.

- Forest products contributed almost $30 billion to Canada's POSITIVE TRADE BALANCE, added over $33 billion to the gross domestic product (GDP), and generated $3.3 billion in new capital investments.

- Total value of forest product EXPORTS reached $39.6 billion.

- DIRECT EMPLOYMENT in the forest sector increased by approximately 14 900 person-years to 376 300 in 2003.

- About two-thirds of Canada's estimated 140 000 SPECIES of plants, animals and micro-organisms live in the forest.

- The FOREST-RELATED TOURISM industry is worth several billion dollars annually.

- There are 15 TERRITORIAL ECOZONES within Canada, containing forest types ranging from the coastal rainforests to sparse and slow-growing forests at the Arctic tree line.

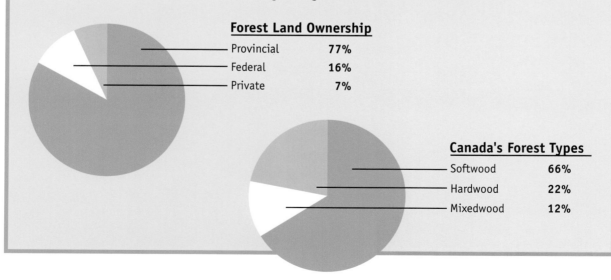

Forest Land Ownership

Provincial	77%
Federal	16%
Private	7%

Canada's Forest Types

Softwood	66%
Hardwood	22%
Mixedwood	12%

YEAR IN REVIEW 2003-2004

As in the past few years, sustainable forest management was high on the agenda of Canada's forest sector in 2003-2004. Cooperation has become central, as governments at all levels work with industry, educational institutions, First Nations and the general public to recognize and strengthen environmental, economic and social values in our forests. More accurate forest information became available through technological advances. Increased forest productivity and secondary value-added production were balanced by heightened attention to sustainability, environmental quality and community values. Efforts to combat destructive invading insects continued. Several new national parks were established, and new conservation programs were initiated. Finally, Canada has consolidated its international leadership by hosting the XII World Forestry Congress and taking responsibility for promoting forest values worldwide.

Combatting Pests

On February 19, 2004, the **Ontario** government announced that it will fund a tree planting program for areas affected by Asian long-horned beetle (Toronto and Vaughan) and emerald ash borer (southwestern Ontario). Trees will be planted to restore or re-green areas where trees have been killed by the beetles or cut as part of the control programs. The funding is intended to leverage financial or in-kind support from federal or municipal partners.

In 2003, **British Columbia**'s mountain pine beetle epidemic increased in intensity and rate of spread, with the result that 4.2 million hectares of pine forests were infested—more than double the area in 2002. The infestation is expected to have economic implications for 30 communities over the next 15 to 20 years. Since 2001, allowable harvest levels in beetle-affected areas have been increased by more than 10 percent of the total provincial harvest to slow the spread of beetles and accelerate the salvage of dead

timber. A search for new markets for beetle-damaged wood has begun. According to an analysis of timber supply impacts, the epidemic will create 500 million cubic metres of dead timber, and despite increased harvests approximately 200 million cubic metres could remain unharvested.

Wildfires and Natural Disasters

Nova Scotia landowners can now access images of their own forests, on the Nova Scotia Department of Natural Resources web site. After Hurricane Juan struck the province in September 2003, visual information was gathered to help the province assess the extent of forest damage. The web site offers a seamless view of more than 680 300 hectares, and includes over 1000 photographs. This service is part of the salvage assistance program for private landowners.

Ontario is implementing a new Forest Fire Management Strategy that takes a more balanced approach to forest fires than the previous strategy. While it continues to focus on protecting human life, property and natural resources from the threat of wildfire, the new strategy also stresses the positive effects of fire as a management tool in achieving ecological objectives.

In 2003, the **Saskatchewan** government released a new *Fire and Forest Insect and Disease Management Policy Framework*. Wise use of fire suppression resources, reduction of wildfire danger, and management of forest insects and disease are the major elements of the new policy framework.

The government of **British Columbia** initiated the Firestorm 2003 Provincial Review in response to the 2003 summer wildfires. After consulting with more than 400 individuals and organizations, the review team presented their analysis and recommendations to the B.C. Cabinet in February 2004. The government is implementing all 42 recommendations in preparation for the next fire season.

In November 2003, the British Columbia Ministry of Forests introduced the *Wildfire Act*, which replaces or streamlines provisions contained in the *Forest Practices Code of B.C. Act*, to ensure the province's communities can be protected from wildfires. The *Wildfire Act* clarifies the responsibilities of all users of the forest, and reduces red tape to enable local response to local conditions, especially in high-risk wildland/urban interface areas.

The **Canadian Council of Forest Ministers** requested a high-level task force to pursue a national approach to risk mitigation and hazard/emergency management. In October 2003, Natural Resources Canada initiated an analysis of the risks posed to Canadians by wildland fire. Natural Resources Canada

has also engaged other federal departments and agencies in discussing opportunities to reduce the risk from wildfires, in partnership with the provinces, territories and municipalities. Discussion is currently under way on the development of a strategic framework for a national forest fire strategy.

Climate Change

On November 6, 2003, the Prime Minister signed a climate change memorandum of understanding with the Forest Products Association of Canada to reduce greenhouse gas emissions. The MOU marks the first agreement with industry to implement the strategy set out in the **Climate Change Plan for Canada**. The agreement covers companies in every region of Canada involved in the production of pulp, newsprint, paperboard and other paper products.

The **Forest 2020 Plantation Demonstration and Assessment Initiative** was launched on November 27, 2003. It will evaluate and develop options that could attract investment, both internationally and domestically, into future Canadian plantations, by taking advantage of the combined benefits of both wood fibre and carbon values. The initiative will also establish a series of plantation sites to test and improve our biological information and demonstrate the contribution from fast-growing trees to help offset greenhouse gas emissions. This program is part of the federal government's Climate Change Plan for Canada to reduce greenhouse gas emissions and address climate change.

SOFTWOOD LUMBER DISPUTE

Canada has continued its efforts to find a resolution to the current softwood lumber dispute. Since May 2002, the United States has been collecting combined countervailing and anti-dumping duties of 27.22 percent on imports of Canadian softwood lumber (shipments from Atlantic Canada are subject only to the 8.43 percent anti-dumping duty).

Canada is pursuing a two-track strategy to resolve the dispute: (1) legal challenges of U.S. trade actions before the World Trade Organization (WTO) and under the North American Free Trade Agreement (NAFTA), and (2) negotiations towards a long-term, policy-based solution. On the legal front, Canada has scored a number of important victories over the past year. NAFTA and WTO panels have ruled that U.S. authorities erred in their calculations of duty rates and have failed to show that imports of softwood lumber from Canada threaten to harm the U.S. domestic industry. Should litigation continue, these cases will likely be concluded sometime in 2005.

Discussions over forest management policies in Canada's provinces have also progressed, but agreement has not yet been reached regarding reforms to such policies or measures that would replace the current duties in the event of a settlement.

Advisory Committees

In October 2003, the **Quebec** government set up the Commission d'étude sur la gestion de la forêt publique québécoise (Commission for the study of Quebec public forest management). The Commission will study the Quebec forestry sector and the development of Quebec's public forests, and will submit its report to the Quebec government in December 2004.

A Forest Science Board was established to advise the Deputy Minister of the **British Columbia** Ministry of

9

XII WORLD FORESTRY CONGRESS

From September 21 to 28, 2003, Canada hosted the XII World Forestry Congress in Quebec City. For the first time, the Congress included three parallel forums: for youth, Aboriginals and private woodlot owners.

The Congress resulted in a Final Statement, adopted by acclamation by the 4000 Congress participants, which reflected the theme of the event: Forests, Source of Life. The Statement affirms the importance of the world's forests for the achievement of important societal objectives and sets out a vision for the future of the world's forests.

Canada was invited to promote the Final Statement to relevant bodies on such strategies as policy, institutional and governance frameworks; partnerships; research, education and capacity building; management; and monitoring. As custodian of the Final Statement, Canada plans to pursue the goals articulated in the Statement and engage the international community in doing so as well.

Forests on the Forest Science Program, as well as to promote and improve the program. The board represents industry, federal and provincial governments, and the forest science community. Results of projects undertaken through the Forest Science Program are disseminated by FORREX—Forest Research Extension Partnership—a unique non-profit organization for forest science extension.

Forest Information

The **Quebec** Ministry of Natural Resources, Wildlife and Parks completed its third inventory program in November 2003. This third eco-forestry inventory comprises ecological data as well as measurement data that will allow more precise evaluation of forest productivity. Quebec has developed a way to reuse sample plots from the second forestry inventory program but achieve greater accuracy of compilations.

In December 2003, the **Ontario** and **British Columbia** governments entered into a partnership to improve the way information about their lands and natural resources is managed. The two provinces will share expertise and policies to improve information management, collection and use of geographic information, cataloguing and distribution of geographic information, and collection of scientific information related to sustainable land management.

The government of **Saskatchewan** invested in improvements to existing forest inventories across the provincial forest, in partnership with federal and provincial agencies, forest companies, First Nations and non-governmental organizations. Base mapping, vegetation inventories, change detection, field sampling programs and enhancement of data management capabilities are included.

The government of the **Northwest Territories** began a pilot project to assess the value of using 1:40 000 kinematic photography to both map forest vegetation and upgrade base map accuracy. The pilot project covers 5000 square kilometres in the Mackenzie Valley near Jean Marie River. If successful, the results will include full specifications for both mapping products, substantial cost savings in mapping forest vegetation, a fully auditable digital product, and rebuilt base maps that achieve greater accuracy.

The government of the Northwest Territories also initiated the Western NWT Biophysical Study to provide baseline biophysical data necessary to assess, mitigate and monitor the environmental impacts of proposed developments in the western NWT. The NWT government is investing $1 million per year for four years to address gaps in information on wildlife, wildlife habitat and forests. Supported research includes studies on boreal caribou, landscape and vegetation classifications, and establishing monitoring plots within the boreal forest.

Canada's **National Forest Inventory** (NFI) is a federal, provincial and territorial partnership aimed at identifying, classifying and documenting all forested land in Canada. Its main goal is to assess and monitor the extent, state and sustainable development of Canada's forests in a timely and accurate manner. The role of the federal government (Natural Resources Canada) is to develop NFI's standards, definitions, procedures and infrastructure, and to conduct the

11

analysis and reporting. The provinces and territories are responsible for developing their inventory designs and providing the data.

Throughout Canada, NFI projects continued during 2003-2004. New agreements were signed between the federal government and Saskatchewan, Manitoba, Prince Edward Island, Newfoundland and Labrador, and the Northwest Territories to further develop the NFI in their jurisdictions. Fieldwork continued in British Columbia, Ontario and Nova Scotia and was completed in New Brunswick and Prince Edward Island. Quebec continued with the development and testing of procedures to analyze its forest inventory to provide the NFI attributes, while the Yukon and Nunavut Territories rely on classified satellite image products to provide data to NFI specifications.

In September 2003, Global Forest Watch Canada released *Canada's Large Intact Forest Landscapes*, which contains maps of Canada's forests based on high-resolution satellite imagery. According to the report, 40 percent of Canada's wild forests have been fragmented by industrial activity, while 60 percent—mostly located in the northern boreal region—remain intact. This report marks the beginning of a partnership agreement between **Natural Resources Canada, the Forest Products Association of Canada, Global Forest Watch Canada and the World Resources Institute** to cooperate in improving and making more accessible Canada's forest information.

Endangered Species

Four additional **Nova Scotia** species—a lichen, a plant, a mammal and a reptile—will now be protected by the province's *Endangered Species Act*. Three of those—the mainland moose, the boreal felt lichen and the Eastern ribbon snake—are considered to be forest-dependent. Two of the new species at risk are classified as endangered, which means they could become extinct in Nova Scotia if steps to reverse the decline of these species are not taken. A total of 24 species have now been placed under the Act's protection in Nova Scotia.

Sustainable Forest Management

In March 2004 the **Newfoundland and Labrador** Department of Natural Resources finalized a new five-year update of its 20-year Provincial Sustainable Forestry Management Strategy. The Strategy provides a clear direction and philosophy for managing the province's forest ecosystems and ensures their management is compatible with national and international sustainable forest management commitments.

The Island Sustainable Forest Partnership, launched in **Prince Edward Island** in July 2003, is associated with the Nova Forest Alliance model forest. The Partnership undertook a number of projects designed to encourage more and better forest stewardship on private lands, including developing a booklet on "Voluntary Sustainable Management Practices for PEI Forest Contractors," demonstrating management options for riparian zones, exploring the potential for a Forest Learning Centre, and offering several Chainsaw Safety and Maintenance courses.

On August 27, 2003, Prince Edward Island acquired a new public forest in Kensington. This 14-hectare public forest will be accessible to all Islanders and will serve as a model for community involvement in forest use and management.

The first component of **Nova Scotia**'s Code of Forest Practice, entitled *A Framework for the Implementation of Sustainable Forest Management*, was made available for public review and comment in April 2003. The Code of Forest Practice is to be a government policy mandatory on Crown land and encouraged on private forest lands. The framework describes the general principles forming the basis for sustainable forest management operations. Following the review and receipt of comments, guidelines and technical manuals will be developed to support the principles.

The year 2003-2004 saw remarkable discussion and public debate about forest policy in **New Brunswick**. The forest community was stirred by the 2002 Jaakko Pöyry report, entitled *New Brunswick Crown Forests: Assessment of Stewardship and Management*, which advocated harvesting more wood from public forests. The public forum, under an all-party Select Committee of the legislature appointed in July 2003, held 13 public hearings. Over 450 submissions, including written and oral presentations, were made to the Select Committee on Wood Supply. The legislative committee tabled its report in summer 2004.

Other activities resulting from the Jaakko Pöyry report included an economic analysis commissioned by the Province of New Brunswick. The report, *The New Brunswick Forest Industry: The Potential Economic Impact of Proposals to Increase the Wood Supply*, was released in December 2003. In addition, the Minister of Natural Resources sought advice from his staff in response to the Jaakko Pöyry report. Comprehensive analysis and research was undertaken, and the resulting Review was released to the public.

In October 2003, the New Brunswick Department of Natural Resources published *Management of New Brunswick's Crown Forest*, a guidebook that takes readers through the management process of New Brunswick Crown forests.

On December 12, 2003, **Quebec** passed Bill 14 to improve the management of that province's public forests. This new bill postpones for a year the date on which forestry management plans come into effect and streamlines forest management programs and activities. The changes also involve amendments to the Peace of the Braves, the agreement signed in February 2002 between the Quebec government and the Grand Council of the Crees.

On January 12, 2004, the **Saskatchewan** government announced that its forestry program's Environmental Management System (EMS) achieved ISO 14001 certification. EMS provides a framework for managing the environmental impacts of activities associated with the province's forest ecosystem program. This is the first province-wide government program in Canada to achieve ISO 14001 certification.

In November 2003, the **Alberta** government decided not to allocate the timber resource on an entire forest management unit of close to 350 000 hectares located northwest of the Chinchaga River. A process

13

for developing a management strategy focusing on the environmental features of the area is under way.

The **Yukon** government, First Nations and Renewable Resource Councils have worked together for the last year to produce, review and consult on a "Discussion Paper" about Yukon forest policy principles. The final discussion paper became available in June 2004; it will help guide the future development of the Yukon's first forestry legislation.

Towards Sustainable Management of the Boreal Forest was launched in September 2003. This book gives a summary of peer-reviewed ecological, economic and social research conducted by the **Sustainable Forest Management Network** over the last seven years.

Defining Sustainable Forest Management in Canada: Criteria and Indicators 2003 was released by the **Canadian Council of Forest Ministers** in September 2003. The document outlines the results of the two-year review to develop more effective indicators for reporting on sustainable forest management in Canada.

Environmental Assessment

One of the most significant developments in forest management in **Ontario** in the past year was the Class Environmental Assessment Approval for Forest Management released June 25, 2003, by Ontario's Minister of the Environment. The approval was based on a comprehensive review of performance under the previous Class Environmental Assessment and extensive public involvement. The approved Environmental Assessment identifies acceptable forest management practices in most Crown forests, covering an area of more than 38.5 million hectares in central and northern Ontario. The approval affects forest policy on public involvement, Aboriginal Peoples, wildlife habitat management, protection of water, forest harvesting, roads, forest renewal, reporting, and scientific research and technology development.

The National Round Table on the Environment and the Economy released *Environment and Sustainable Development Indicators for Canada* in May 2003. Six indicators are contained in the report: freshwater quality, air quality, greenhouse gas emissions, **forest cover**, wetlands and human capital (educational attainment of the population). These indicators will track, at the national level, the impacts of current economic practices on the natural and human assets that will be needed by future generations of Canadians. The "forest cover" indicator, to be reported annually, measures the percentage of Canada's total area covered by forests.

Conservation

Newfoundland and Labrador residents can now report illegal activity through the province's Department of Natural Resources web site. Conservation officers are thus provided with a valuable tool to apprehend those engaged in illegal activities that threaten the province's forest and wildlife resources. This proactive approach towards resource protection will help sustain the province's forests and wildlife for future generations.

14

More than 100 hectares of Blanding's turtle habitat are being protected. The Blanding's turtle is listed as endangered under the **Nova Scotia** *Endangered Species Act*. Bowater Mersey Paper Company Limited has established a new conservation area under its Unique Areas Program. The newly protected area is on Bowater lands adjacent to McGowan Lake.

In September 2003, the **Quebec** government gave "exceptional forest ecosystem" status to 37 forests covering a total area of 3700 hectares. These consist of rare forests, old-growth forests, and shelter forests for threatened or vulnerable species. The Quebec network of forests protected under this status now includes 63 units covering 8000 hectares.

On June 12, 2003, the **Ontario** government and Ducks Unlimited Canada, building on their many years of cooperative efforts, agreed to participate in a new $2-million match-funding project to protect wetlands in southern Ontario. They will invest in a series of wetland interpretation and rehabilitation projects over the next three years.

On August 13, 2003, the Ontario Ministry of Natural Resources designated the Eramosa Karst in Hamilton as a provincially significant earth science Area of Natural and Scientific Interest. The designation recognizes the importance of this geological formation for natural heritage protection, appreciation, scientific study and education.

A memorandum of understanding was signed on March 19, 2004, between the Province of **Manitoba** and the Government of Canada towards the establishment of a national park in Manitoba's northern Interlake region. This initiative is part of the five-year federal action plan to create 10 new national parks.

The **Northwest Territories** recently produced *Northwest Territories Biodiversity Action Plan: Major Initiatives on Biodiversity*, which lists current activities related to the territories' biodiversity. The NWT Biodiversity Action Plan's objective is to review each goal of the Canadian Biodiversity Strategy from the territories' perspective.

Also in the Northwest Territories, the Protected Areas Strategy Secretariat completed the *Protected Areas Strategy 2004-2009 Action Plan* report in October 2003. The action plan describes the strategic enhancement needed over the next five years to identify, review, evaluate and establish interim protection for a network of protected areas in the Mackenzie Valley.

As part of a forestry conservation project, a partnership agreement to identify **High Conservation Value Forests** (HCVFs) was signed on November 27, 2003, between the World Wildlife Fund Canada and Abitibi-Consolidated. HCVFs are forests of critical importance because of their high environmental, socio-economic, biodiversity or landscape values. Over the entire 18 million hectares of Abitibi-Consolidated licensed forests, appropriate areas for HCVFs will be identified. The project will assist in establishing a network of protected areas in Quebec, Ontario, Newfoundland and Labrador, and British Columbia where native plant and animal species can thrive.

15

Canadian FOREST MANAGEMENT CERTIFICATION Status

According to the June 6, 2004 Coalition certification status report, 143 million hectares of forest land across the country, representing an annual allowable cut of approximately 124 million cubic metres, have been certified, if all certifications to ISO, CSA, SFI and FSC are included. Otherwise, certifications to Sustainable Forest Management (SFM) standards including CSA, SFI and FSC come to approximately 57.7 million hectares of forest land, representing an annual allowable cut of almost 66 million cubic metres.

STANDARD USED	AREA CERTIFIED (IN HECTARES)
ISO 14001 *International Organization for Standardization*	**127.1 million**
World-wide most recognized Environmental Management System Standard, helping organizations to better manage the impact of their activities on the environment and to demonstrate sound environmental management.	
CSA *The Canadian Standards Association—Canada's National Sustainable Forest Management Standards*	**32.9 million**
Based on nationally and internationally recognized criteria for sustainable forest management. Addresses environmental, social and economic issues and requires a rigorous public participation.	
SFI *Sustainable Forestry Initiative Program—developed by the American Forestry & Paper Association*	**21.4 million**
Includes environmental objectives and performance measures and integrates the growing and harvesting of trees with the protection of wildlife, plants, and soil and water quality, along with other conservation goals.	
FSC *Forest Stewardship Council*	**4.2 million**
Supports environmentally appropriate, socially beneficial and economically viable management of the world's forests. Also supports the development of national and regional standards.	

Source: Canadian Sustainable Forestry Certification Coalition (Internet site: www.sfms.com)

If a forest area has been certified to more than one of the three SFM standards (CSA, FSC and SFI), the area is only counted once; hence the total of certifications for SFM standards may be less than the sum of the individual totals for these standards.

The Conservation of Natural Heritage Program was launched in May 2001 to encourage Canadians to undertake stewardship of public and private land and water. The report resulting from the first phase, *Securing Canada's Natural Capital: A Vision for Nature Conservation in the 21st Century* (State of the Debate report), was released in June 2003. The second phase of the program focuses on conservation in the **boreal forest**. A task force is studying three boreal forest areas of Canada with significant biodiversity: the Muskwa-Kechika Management Areas in northeastern British Columbia; the Alberta-Pacific Forest Management Agreement Area along the Saskatchewan border west to Lesser Slave Lake; and the Abitibi Region along the Quebec-Ontario border.

The **Canadian Boreal Initiative** (CBI), a national, non-governmental organization, was established in January 2003 to promote boreal conservation and sustainable development. On December 1, CBI released the *Boreal Forest Conservation Framework*, which is based on a shared vision to sustain the ecological and cultural integrity of the Canadian boreal forest region. The framework was developed in concert with leading conservation organizations, resource companies and First Nations, and endorsed by the Forest Products Association of Canada. It proposes a network of large interconnected protected areas covering approximately half of Canada's boreal region.

Forest Industry

Changes were made to two sets of **Nova Scotia** forestry regulations that oversee the commercial buying and selling of wood, the *Registration and Statistical Returns Regulations* and the *Forest Sustainability Regulations*. These regulations, which establish the registry of buyers of primary forest products, require annual registration and submission of statistical returns. The proposed changes should make the regulations easier to follow based on feedback from those who use them. They include simplifying some of the

reporting requirements, clarifying who is an exporter of wood and defining wood chips.

As of February 29, 2004, a new market-based timber pricing system for the coastal forest sector in **British Columbia** determines stumpage prices. The market pricing system will help revitalize the industry by ensuring competitive stumpage rates that better reflect global markets and local harvesting costs.

Other Values of the Forest

On March 24, 2004, the **Prince Edward Island** Public Forest Council released *The Forest Is More Than Just a Bunch of Trees*. This new 22-minute video highlights the Island's public forests as well as the many values they offer.

New Brunswick has developed a strategy for encouraging more value-added activities involving natural resources. To this end, a new maple sugary leasing policy was developed in 2003 which encourages value-added initiatives. Currently about 7000 hectares of Crown land are used for tapping trees to make maple syrup. The government has allocated an additional 2000 hectares to syrup producers to help them transform the harvest into a saleable product.

In February 2004, the **Quebec** Ministry of Natural Resources, Wildlife and Parks adopted a program allocating public land under forestry management for blueberry fields. This program will make forestry development land accessible for inter-cropping blueberry fields with forested areas. The development of

60m-wide strips of blueberry fields alternated with 40m-wide forested strips managed intensively for wood production is an innovative agroforestry concept and a model of integrated management of forest resources.

In March 2004, the Quebec government confirmed its financial contribution to the Centre intégré en pâtes et papiers (integrated pulp and paper centre) project at the Université du Québec à Trois-Rivières. Quebec joins the Canadian government, educational institutions and private-sector companies supporting this project. The Centre will bring together key stakeholders in the pulp and paper industry and will play a vital role in pulp and paper education and research.

In 2003 **Manitoba** created a Sustainable Forestry Unit. It will increase value-added processing in the forest sector (including timber and non-timber forest products), and foster interaction between primary and secondary industry. The Unit will also encourage Aboriginal forestry developments, including resource co-management, business ownership and economic development (particularly training and employment).

In March 2004, Manitoba announced its membership to Forintek's Value-Added and Wood Technology Program. The province's wood products manufacturers now have access to industry specialists, technological solutions, latest research and other services offered in the program.

Innovation

On March 3, 2004, the **New Brunswick** Community College in Miramichi announced it will acquire a high-tech forest harvestor/processor and simulator to modernize the delivery of its forest operator program.

Thanks partly to this acquisition, the college will have one of the best forestry schools in the region and will attract students across Atlantic Canada. At the Université de Moncton, a new Bachelor's Program in Applied Agroforestry was introduced. The program will train professionals to integrate forestry into the agricultural landscape, thus contributing to the sustainable development of farmland and forest land.

In 2003, the **Canadian Forest Innovation Council**, an executive body composed of representatives from industry and the federal and provincial/territorial governments, was established. The Council seeks to improve the innovative capacity of the Canadian forest sector to promote industry profitability, environmental quality and community stability. It provides a forum for a national innovation agenda and promotes Canadian forest sector innovation goals.

Aboriginal Activities

Saskatchewan Environment and seven First Nations signed a joint memorandum of understanding in July 2003. The MOU focuses on economic development opportunities in the First Nations' traditional lands in the Island Forests area and surrounding fringe forests.

In October 2003, an area-based Term Supply Licence (TSL) was issued to the Kitsaki-Zelensky Partnership, an alliance between Kitsaki Management Limited Partnership, the business arm of the Lac La Ronge Indian Band, and Zelensky Brothers Sawmill. The area of the TSL was previously under licence to Weyerhaeuser Saskatchewan, but was relinquished in 1999.

The Canadian Forestry Association has designated the town of Lac La Biche and Lakeland County in Alberta as the **Forest Capital of Canada for 2004.** This designation allows the region to celebrate its historic and forward-looking ties to the forest with a year-long campaign of special events and promotion. Established in 1979, the Forest Capital of Canada program focuses on the valuable role forests play in the socio-economic and environmental health of Canadian communities.

The **Tli Cho First Nations**, the government of the **Northwest Territories** and the **Government of Canada** signed a land claims and self-government agreement covering the land area of the Tli Cho peoples (Dogrib First Nation). The agreement provides for management and title over the lands they hold, and participation in natural resource management over other lands in the agreement area. It also provides for the application of Tli Cho laws to forest management and natural resource management. The Tli Cho agreement represents a significant advance, being a settlement of both land and self-government.

On January 30, 2004, the **Yukon** government and the Kaska First Nations signed an Agreement in Principle to establish a business relationship. A Forest Authority will be assigned the Annual Allowable Cut within the Kaska First Nations Traditional Territory, for both public and First Nations lands. The Authority's mandate will be to develop a small, sustainable forest economy in southeast Yukon.

On March 19, 2004, the Yukon government entered into a partnership with the Champagne and Aishihik First Nation to develop a plan that will address forests affected by the spruce bark beetle in southwest Yukon. The plan will have three primary focus areas:

fuel abatement (protection from wildfires), economic opportunities and forest renewal.

On September 3, 2003, **Nunavut, Northwest Territories** and **Yukon** signed a Northern Cooperation Accord. The three-year accord is intended to strengthen the North of Canada's voice on the national stage in the areas of economy, devolution, Aboriginal rights, environment and social policy.

An Inuit Impact and Benefit Agreement (IIBA) was signed on August 23, 2003, between the Government of Canada, the government of Nunavut and the Kivalliq Inuit Association of Nunavut towards the establishment of a national park in **Nunavut**. The new Ukkusiksalik National Park—Canada's 41st national park—is named after the soapstone found in the area, and is home to a large number of caribou, polar bear, musk oxen and other species. The park includes 2 050 000 hectares of eskers, mudflats, cliffs, rolling tundra banks and unique coastal regions. Part of the five-year federal action plan to create 10 new national parks, the IIBA also protects Inuit rights in the park and offers business and employment opportunities to the local Inuit communities.

19

MERGERS and ACQUISITIONS in the Forest Sector

The pace of mergers and acquisitions increased in 2003 in the Canadian forest industry, following a slowdown of activity in 2002 and early 2003. One significant transaction was Canfor's acquisition of Slocan, a $630-million deal announced in November 2003 and finalized in March 2004. The new Canfor is now the second largest lumber producer in North America (Weyerhaeuser is the largest). Other recent activity, such as Riverside's $100-million purchase of Lignum, has also signalled a renewed desire by Canadian firms to grow through mergers and acquisitions.

Consolidation is seen by many in the Canadian forest products industry as a way to improve international competitiveness. Even the largest Canadian companies are relatively small in international terms; some hold a significant market share in select product lines such as softwood lumber and newsprint, but lack overall size in relation to more integrated international firms. Consolidation provides an opportunity for companies to rationalize operations, reducing production costs and thus improving their cost competitiveness. Increased size also makes it easier to attract capital for modernization and expansion, important in an industry where capital expenditures have fallen well below depreciation in recent years. These considerations must be balanced against the disadvantages consolidation brings to competition within the domestic market.

Regulatory issues can influence merger and acquisition activity on both a provincial and a federal level.

- The *Competition Act*, administered by Industry Canada's Competition Bureau, is aimed at stopping anti-competitive practices in the marketplace.

The act includes provisions for mergers involving Canadian business entities. In the recent Canfor-Slocan merger, the Competition Bureau required that Canfor divest its Fort St. James sawmill, located near Prince George, British Columbia. The requirement resulted from concerns that the merger could lessen local competition in timber, lumber and wood chip markets.

- The government of British Columbia, in its movement towards a more market-based tenure system in B.C., has announced that more timber will be sold through public auctions. These auctions will then be used to set the rates for Crown timber paid by licensees and other users, creating a more market-based pricing system. Consequently, the B.C. government is paying attention to mergers and acquisitions in the industry, as these have the potential to reduce regional competition for wood fibre.

Regulatory issues notwithstanding, it appears likely that Canadian firms will continue to look to mergers and acquisitions as a way to rationalize production and capitalize on larger economies of scale.

DATE	COMPANY MAKING ACQUISITION	COMPANY/OPERATION SOLD	ACTION	FINANCES	DETAILS OF ACTION
Feb. '02	North West B.C. Timber and Pulp Co.	Skeena Cellulose Inc.	Sale	$8 million	B.C.: 1 pulp mill; 4 sawmills; and log chipping facilities
April '02	Tembec Inc. and SGF Rexfor known as Temrex Forest Products L.P.	Produits Forestiers St-Alphonse Inc. and Nouvelle Sawmill	Joint venture	$65.6 million	Que.: 2 sawmills

20

DATE	COMPANY MAKING ACQUISITION	COMPANY/OPERATION SOLD	ACTION	FINANCES	DETAILS OF ACTION
April '02	Nexfor Inc.	International Paper	Sale	Undisclosed	U.S.: 3 oriented strandboard mills
June '02	SFK Pulp Fund	Abitibi-Consolidated, St-Félicien	Sale	Undisclosed	Que.: 1 pulp mill
June '02	Cascades Inc.	American Tissue Inc.	Sale	US$33 million	U.S.: 1 tissue mill; 2 conversion sites; and 1 paper machine
Oct. '02	West Fraser Timber Co. Ltd.	Daishowa Canada Co. Ltd.	Sale	Undisclosed	B.C.: 1 pulp mill
Oct. '02	Tembec Inc.	Louisiana Pacific, Chetwynd	Sale	$50 million* * environmental clean-up, capital expenditures and work capital costs	B.C.: 1 pulp mill
Nov. '02	Taiga Forest Products Ltd.	Louisiana Pacific, Rocklin, Calif.	Sale	Undisclosed	U.S.: 1 distribution centre
Dec. '02	Columbia Forest Products, Portland, Ore.	Weyerhaeuser Company, Nipigon Multiply	Sale	Undisclosed	Ont.: 1 hardwood plywood mill
Dec. '02	Bois Omega Ltée, Lac-Supérieur, Qué.	Beaman Lumber, Winchester, N.H.	Sale	Undisclosed	U.S.: 1 sawmill
April '03	Groupe Lebel, Rivière-du-Loup, Qué.	Poutrelles Internationales, Pohenegamook	Sale	Undisclosed	Que.: 1 I-joist mill
April '03	Canfor Corp.	Daaquam Lumber Inc. and Produits Forestiers Anticosti	Sale	$50 million	Que.: 1 lumber manufacturing; and 1 harvesting operation
August '03	Tembec Inc.	Nexfor Inc., La Sarre and Senne-terre	Sale	$49.2 million	Que.: 2 sawmills
Oct. '03	Tembec Inc.	Weyerhaeuser Company, Chapleau	Sale	$26 million	Ont.: 1 sawmill
Nov. '03	Canfor Corp.	Slocan Forest Products Ltd.	Merger	$630 million	B.C.: 10 sawmills; 1 plywood mill; 1 oriented strandboard mill; 1 pulp mill; 1 lumber remanufac-turing; and 1 lami-nated beam
Jan. '04	Tolko Industries	Weyerhaeuser Company, Slave Lake	Sale	$56 million	Alta.: 1 oriented strandboard mill
Feb. '04	Riverside Forest Products Ltd.	Lignum	Sale	$100 million	B.C.: 1 sawmill; and 20 wholesale distributors of forest products across Canada and the U.S.
March '04	C&C Wood Products Ltd.	Weyerhaeuser Company, Grande Cache	Sale	Undisclosed	Alta.: 1 sawmill
April '04	Ainsworth Lumber Co.	Voyageur Panel Limited, Barwick	Sale	US$193 million	Ont.: 1 oriented strandboard mill
April '04	J.D. Irving Limited	Deniso Lebel, Kedgwick	Sale	Undisclosed	N.B.: 1 sawmill
May '04	LaPointe Partners	Doman Industries Ltd., Port Alice	Sale	Undisclosed	B.C.: 1 pulp mill

21

Forest and Other Wooded Land

Canada's Forest Inventory 2001
Natural Resources Canada
Canadian Forest Service

CANADA

Population (2004)
31.8 million

Total area
998.5 million ha

Land area
909.4 million ha

Maple Tree

Forest and other wooded land
401.5 million ha

National parks
26.5 million ha

Park attendance
16.0 million person-visits

% of Area	Area (M of ha)
0–<5	1.2
5–<20	7.9
20–<40	21.6
40–<60	40.9
60–<80	86.2
80–100	243.7
Total	**401.5**

FOREST RESOURCE

Ownership	
Provincial	77%
Federal	16%
Private	7%
Forest type	
Softwood	66%
Hardwood	22%
Mixedwood	12%
Annual allowable cut (2001)[a]	236.8 million m³
Harvest (volume) Industrial roundwood (2002)[b]	189.2 million m³
Harvest (area) Industrial roundwood (2002)	972 303 ha
Status of harvested Crown land (2001)[c]	
Stocked (87%)	16.2 million ha
Understocked (13%)	2.4 million ha
Forest regeneration on public land	16.2 million ha
Area defoliated by insects and beetle-killed trees (2002)[d]	18.2 million ha
Number of fires (2003)[e]	8 218
Area burned (2003)[e]	1.6 million ha

NON-TIMBER FOREST PRODUCTS

Production value	
Maple products (2003)	31.3 million litres
Christmas trees (2001)	4.1 million
Wildlife pelts (minus seals) (2001)	1.0 million

MAJOR VALUE-ADDED WOOD PRODUCTS

Value of shipments (2001)	$4.5 billion
Doors and windows	$1.9 billion
Framing products	$868.2 million
Prefabricated buildings	$643.1 million
Mobile houses	$376.6 million
Other products	$702.8 million

FOREST INDUSTRY

Value of exports (2003)	$39.6 billion
Softwood lumber	$8.5 billion
Newsprint	$5.6 billion
Wood pulp	$6.8 billion
Waferboard	$2.8 billion
Other paper and paperboard	$6.5 billion
Converted paper	$1.0 billion
Other products	$8.4 billion
Major export markets (2003)	$39.6 billion
United States	$31.0 billion
European Union	$2.7 billion
Japan	$2.2 billion
China	$1.0 billion
South and Central America	$0.6 billion
Other countries	$2.2 billion
Balance of trade (2003)	$29.7 billion
Contribution to GDP (gross domestic product) (2003)	$33.7 billion
Value of shipments	not available
Exported	not available
Sold domestically	not available
Number of establishments	not available
Logging	not available
Wood product manufacturing (2001)	3 740
Paper manufacturing (2001)	850
Direct employment (2003)	376 300
Wages and salaries	not available
New investments (2003)	$3.3 billion

[a, b, c, d, e] *see page 38*

22

BRITISH COLUMBIA

Western Red Cedar

Population (2004)
4.2 million
Total area
94.5 million ha
Land area
92.5 million ha
Forest and other wooded land
64.1 million ha

FOREST RESOURCE

Ownership		
Provincial		96%
Federal		1%
Private		3%
Forest type		
Softwood		82%
Hardwood		5%
Mixedwood		13%
Annual allowable cut (2001)[a]		81.5 million m³
Harvest (volume) Industrial roundwood (2002)[b]		73.6 million m³
Harvest (area) Industrial roundwood (2002)		189 277 ha
Status of harvested Crown land (2001)[c]		
Stocked	(82%)	3.6 million ha
Understocked	(18%)	770 000 ha
Area defoliated by insects and beetle-killed trees (2002)[d]		4.0 million ha
Number of fires (2003)[e]		2 447
Area burned (2003)[e]		266 412 ha

FOREST INDUSTRY

Value of exports (2003)	$12.6 billion
Softwood lumber	$5.3 billion
Newsprint	$0.6 billion
Wood pulp	$2.8 billion
Waferboard	$0.6 billion
Other paper and paperboard	$1.2 billion
Converted paper	$16.2 million
Other products	$2.1 billion
Major export markets (2003)	$12.6 billion
United States	$7.8 billion
European Union	$1.0 billion
Japan	$1.9 billion
China	$0.6 billion
South and Central America	$0.2 billion
Other countries	$1.1 billion
Balance of trade (2003)	$11.4 billion
Value of shipments	not available
Logging	not available
Wood product manufacturing (2001)	$11.2 billion
Paper manufacturing (2001)	$6.4 billion
Number of establishments	not available
Logging	not available
Wood product manufacturing (2001)	900
Paper manufacturing (2001)	85
Direct employment (2003)	91 600
Wages and salaries	not available
Logging	not available
Wood product manufacturing (2001)	$1.7 billion
Paper manufacturing (2001)	$871.9 million
New investments (2003)	$0.6 billion

ALBERTA

Lodgepole Pine

Population (2004)
3.2 million
Total area
66.2 million ha
Land area
64.2 million ha
Forest and other wooded land
36.4 million ha

FOREST RESOURCE

Ownership	
Provincial	89%
Federal	8%
Private	3%
Forest type	
Softwood	50%
Hardwood	32%
Mixedwood	18%
Annual allowable cut (2001)[a]	26.2 million m³
Harvest (volume) Industrial roundwood (2002)[b]	24.6 million m³
Harvest (area) Industrial roundwood (2002)	68 430 ha
Status of harvested Crown land[c]	
Stocked	not available
Understocked	not available
Area defoliated by insects and beetle-killed trees (2002)[d]	4.2 million ha
Number of fires (2003)[e]	1 191
Area burned (2003)[e]	55 482 ha

FOREST INDUSTRY

Value of exports (2003)	$2.8 billion
Softwood lumber	$580.4 million
Newsprint	$114.5 million
Wood pulp	$1.2 billion
Waferboard	$571.1 million
Other paper and paperboard	$18.3 million
Converted paper	$20.8 million
Other products	$254.5 million
Major export markets (2003)	$2.8 billion
United States	$1.9 billion
European Union	$163.1 million
Japan	$238.5 million
China	$148.3 million
South and Central America	$16.3 million
Other countries	$257.7 million
Balance of trade (2003)	$2.5 billion
Value of shipments (2001)	not available
Logging	not available
Wood product manufacturing	$2.7 billion
Paper manufacturing	$1.7 billion
Number of establishments	not available
Logging	not available
Wood product manufacturing (2001)	286
Paper manufacturing (2001)	35
Direct employment (2003)	25 300
Wages and salaries	not available
Logging	not available
Wood product manufacturing (2001)	$443.4 million
Paper manufacturing (2001)	$206.1 million
New investments (2003)	$0.2 billion

23

SASKATCHEWAN

Population (2004)
1.0 million
Total area
65.1 million ha
Land area
59.2 million ha
Forest and other wooded land
24.3 million ha

White Birch

FOREST RESOURCE

Ownership	
Provincial	90%
Federal	4%
Private	6%
Forest type	
Softwood	47%
Hardwood	16%
Mixedwood	37%
Annual allowable cut (2001)[a]	8.9 million m³
Harvest (volume) Industrial roundwood (2002)[b]	4.3 million m³
Harvest (area) Industrial roundwood (2002)	23 222 ha
Status of harvested Crown land[c]	
Stocked	not available
Understocked	not available
Area defoliated by insects and beetle-killed trees (2002)[d]	669 591 ha
Number of fires (2003)[e]	642
Area burned (2003)[e]	126 191 ha

FOREST INDUSTRY

Value of exports (2003)	$643.4 million
Softwood lumber	$84.3 million
Newsprint	$0.1 million
Wood pulp	$284.4 million
Waferboard	$117.3 million
Other paper and paperboard	$112.6 million
Converted paper	$16.5 million
Other products	$28.2 million
Major export markets (2003)	$643.4 million
United States	$456.0 million
European Union	$94.3 million
China	$22.5 million
South and Central America	$12.5 million
Japan	$11.6 million
Other countries	$46.5 million
Balance of trade (2003)	$543.0 million
Value of shipments	not available
Logging	not available
Wood product manufacturing (2001)	$326.4 million
Paper manufacturing (2001)	$496.2 million
Number of establishments	not available
Logging	not available
Wood product manufacturing (2001)	59
Paper manufacturing (2001)	9
Direct employment (2003)	6 198
Wages and salaries	not available
Logging	not available
Wood product manufacturing (2001)	$64.3 million
Paper manufacturing (2001)	$76.2 million
New investments (2003)	not available

MANITOBA

Population (2004)
1.2 million
Total area
64.8 million ha
Land area
55.4 million ha
Forest and other wooded land
36.0 million ha

White Spruce

FOREST RESOURCE

Ownership	
Provincial	95%
Federal	2%
Private	3%
Forest type	
Softwood	74%
Hardwood	15%
Mixedwood	11%
Annual allowable cut (2001)[a]	9.6 million m³
Harvest (volume) Industrial roundwood (2002)[b]	2.0 million m³
Harvest (area) Industrial roundwood (2002)	15 042 ha
Status of harvested Crown land (2001)[c]	
Stocked (95%)	308 000 ha
Understocked (5%)	15 000 ha
Area defoliated by insects and beetle-killed trees (2002)[d]	101 821 ha
Number of fires (2003)[e]	1 148
Area burned (2003)[e]	430 170 ha

FOREST INDUSTRY

Value of exports (2003)	$640.0 million
Softwood lumber	$54.2 million
Newsprint	$140.6 million
Wood pulp	$1.2 million
Waferboard	$128.1 million
Other paper and paperboard	$79.7 million
Converted paper	$28.7 million
Other products	$207.5 million
Major export markets (2003)	$640.0 million
United States	$629.9 million
European Union	$1.2 million
Japan	$1.5 million
South and Central America	$2.6 million
Other countries	$4.8 million
Balance of trade (2003)	$263.7 million
Value of shipments	not available
Logging	not available
Wood product manufacturing (2001)	$635.1 million
Paper manufacturing (2001)	$590.1 million
Number of establishments	not available
Logging	not available
Wood product manufacturing (2001)	76
Paper manufacturing (2001)	30
Direct employment (2003)	8 900
Wages and salaries	not available
Logging	not available
Wood product manufacturing (2001)	$118.3 million
Paper manufacturing (2001)	$104.5 million
New investments (2003)	not available

ONTARIO

Eastern White Pine

Population (2004)
12.3 million
Total area
107.6 million ha
Land area
91.8 million ha
Forest and other wooded land
68.3 million ha

FOREST RESOURCE

Ownership		
Provincial		91%
Federal		1%
Private		8%
Forest type		
Softwood		58%
Hardwood		16%
Mixedwood		26%
Annual allowable cut (2002)[a]		293 288 ha
Harvest (volume) Industrial roundwood (2002)[b]		26.3 million m³
Harvest (area) Industrial roundwood (2002)		184 322 ha
Status of harvested Crown land (2001)[c]		
Stocked	(88%)	4.3 million ha
Understocked	(12%)	597 000 ha
Area defoliated by insects and beetle-killed trees (2002)[d]		8.8 million ha
Number of fires (2003)[e]		1 015
Area burned (2003)[e]		314 219 ha

FOREST INDUSTRY

Value of exports (2003)	$8.5 billion
Softwood lumber	$0.6 billion
Newsprint	$1.3 billion
Wood pulp	$0.9 billion
Waferboard	$0.8 billion
Other paper and paperboard	$1.7 billion
Converted paper	$0.6 billion
Other products	$2.6 billion
Major export markets (2003)	$8.5 billion
United States	$8.2 billion
European Union	$124.5 million
South and Central America	$64.9 million
China	$25.8 million
Japan	$7.7 million
Other countries	$96.8 million
Balance of trade (2003)	$2.8 billion
Value of shipments (2001)	not available
Logging	not available
Wood product manufacturing	$6.0 billion
Paper manufacturing	$12.0 billion
Number of establishments	not available
Logging	not available
Wood product manufacturing (2001)	912
Paper manufacturing (2001)	385
Direct employment (2003)	88 100
Wages and salaries	not available
Logging	not available
Wood product manufacturing (2001)	$1.0 billion
Paper manufacturing (2001)	$1.8 billion
New investments (2003)	$0.6 billion

QUEBEC

Yellow Birch

Population (2004)
7.5 million
Total area
154.2 million ha
Land area
136.5 million ha
Forest and other wooded land
84.6 million ha

FOREST RESOURCE

Ownership		
Provincial		89%
Private		11%
Forest type		
Softwood		73%
Hardwood		11%
Mixedwood		16%
Annual allowable cut (2001)[a]		55.9 million m³
Harvest (volume) Industrial roundwood (2002)[b]		39.6 million m³
Harvest (area) Industrial roundwood (2002)		309 195 ha
Status of harvested Crown land (2001)[c]		
Stocked	(97%)	5.9 million ha
Understocked	(3%)	159 000 ha
Area defoliated by insects and beetle-killed trees (2002)[d]		280 983 ha
Number of fires (2003)[e]		716
Area burned (2003)[e]		87 860 ha

FOREST INDUSTRY

Value of exports (2003)	$10.7 billion
Softwood lumber	$1.2 billion
Newsprint	$2.6 billion
Wood pulp	$0.9 billion
Waferboard	$0.4 billion
Other paper and paperboard	$2.5 billion
Converted paper	$0.3 billion
Other products	$2.8 billion
Major export markets (2003)	$10.7 billion
United States	$9.2 billion
European Union	$797.0 million
Japan	$29.1 million
South and Central America	$157.8 million
China	$137.1 million
Other countries	$360.6 million
Balance of trade (2003)	$8.8 billion
Value of shipments (2001)	not available
Logging	not available
Wood product manufacturing	$8.4 billion
Paper manufacturing	$12.2 billion
Number of establishments	not available
Logging	not available
Wood product manufacturing (2001)	1 129
Paper manufacturing (2001)	251
Direct employment (2003)	118 300
Wages and salaries	not available
Logging	not available
Wood product manufacturing (2001)	$1.3 billion
Paper manufacturing (2001)	$1.6 billion
New investments (2003)	$1.3 billion

25

NEW BRUNSWICK

Population (2004)
750 096
Total area
7.3 million ha
Land area
7.1 million ha
Forest and other wooded land
6.2 million ha

Balsam Fir

FOREST RESOURCE

Ownership		
Provincial		48%
Federal		2%
Private		50%
Forest type		
Softwood		44%
Hardwood		25%
Mixedwood		31%
Annual allowable cut (2001)[a]		11.0 million m³
Harvest (volume) Industrial roundwood (2002)[b]		10.1 million m³
Harvest (area) Industrial roundwood (2002)		105 834 ha
Status of harvested Crown land (2001)[c]		
Stocked	(95%)	638 000 ha
Understocked	(5%)	35 000 ha
Area defoliated by insects and beetle-killed trees (2002)[dd]		2 124 ha
Number of fires (2003)[e]		228
Area burned (2003)[e]		237 ha

FOREST INDUSTRY

Value of exports (2003)	$2.3 billion
Softwood lumber	$431.5 million
Newsprint	$217.9 million
Wood pulp	$523.2 million
Waferboard	$101.3 million
Other paper and paperboard	$653.3 million
Converted paper	$32.1 million
Other products	$324.0 million
Major export markets (2003)	$2.3 billion
United States	$1.9 billion
European Union	$154.9 million
Japan	$41.2 million
South and Central America	$21.0 million
China	$6.5 million
Other countries	$159.4 million
Balance of trade (2003)	$2.0 billion
Value of shipments	not available
Logging	not available
Wood product manufacturing (2001)	$1.4 billion
Paper manufacturing (2001)	$2.2 billion
Number of establishments	not available
Logging	not available
Wood product manufacturing (2001)	165
Paper manufacturing (2001)	27
Direct employment (2003)	20 400
Wages and salaries	not available
Logging	not available
Wood product manufacturing (2001)	$217.3 million
Paper manufacturing (2001)	$307.0 million
New investments (2003)	not available

NOVA SCOTIA

Population (2004)
936 892
Total area
5.5 million ha
Land area
5.3 million ha
Forest and other wooded land
4.3 million ha

Red Spruce

FOREST RESOURCE

Ownership		
Provincial		29%
Federal		3%
Private		68%
Forest type		
Softwood		58%
Hardwood		13%
Mixedwood		29%
Annual allowable cut (2001)[a]		6.7 million m³
Harvest (volume) Industrial roundwood (2002)[b]		6.0 million m³
Harvest (area) Industrial roundwood (2002)		49 959 ha
Status of harvested Crown land (2001)[c]		
Stocked	(97%)	203 000 ha
Understocked	(3%)	6 400 ha
Area defoliated by insects and beetle-killed trees (2002)[d]		17 520 ha
Number of fires (2003)[e]		274
Area burned (2003)[e]		1 257 ha

FOREST INDUSTRY

Value of exports (2003)	$923.1 million
Softwood lumber	$163.5 million
Newsprint	$235.8 million
Wood pulp	$191.0 million
Waferboard	$0.1 million
Other paper and paperboard	$244.4 million
Converted paper	$10.1 million
Other products	$78.1 million
Major export markets (2003)	$923.1 million
United States	$670.2 million
European Union	$97.4 million
Japan	$8.2 million
South and Central America	$73.6 million
China	$4.1 million
Other countries	$69.6 million
Balance of trade (2003)	$873.4 million
Value of shipments	not available
Logging	not available
Wood product manufacturing (2001)	$537.8 million
Paper manufacturing (2001)	$1.0 billion
Number of establishments	not available
Logging	not available
Wood product manufacturing (2001)	126
Paper manufacturing (2001)	14
Direct employment (2003)	13 360
Wages and salaries	not available
Logging	not available
Wood product manufacturing (2001)	$88.4 million
Paper manufacturing (2001)	$132.2 million
New investments (2003)	not available

PRINCE EDWARD ISLAND

Red Oak

Population (2004)
138 102
Total area
0.6 million ha
Land area
0.6 million ha
**Forest and other
wooded land**
0.3 million ha

FOREST RESOURCE

Ownership	
Provincial	8%
Federal	1%
Private	91%
Forest type	
Softwood	24%
Hardwood	29%
Mixedwood	47%
Annual allowable cut (2001)[a]	0.5 million m^3
Harvest (volume) Industrial roundwood (2002)[b]	0.4 million m^3
Harvest (area) Industrial roundwood (2002)	4 903 ha
Status of harvested Crown land (2001)[c]	
Stocked (100%)	54 800 ha
Area defoliated by insects and beetle-killed trees[d]	not available
Number of fires (2003)[e]	14
Area burned (2003)[e]	12 ha

FOREST INDUSTRY

Value of exports (2003)	$13.0 million
Softwood lumber	$11.7 million
Other paper and paperboard	$45 841
Converted paper	$32 497
Other products	$1.2 million
Major export markets (2003)	$13.0 million
United States	$12.8 million
European Union	$0.2 million
Balance of trade (2003)	$13.0 million
Value of shipments	not available
Logging	not available
Wood product manufacturing (2001)	$46.2 million
Paper manufacturing (2001)	not available
Number of establishments	not available
Logging	not available
Wood product manufacturing (2001)	15
Paper manufacturing (2001)	5
Direct employment (2003)	740
Wages and salaries	not available
Logging	not available
Wood product manufacturing (2001)	$8.0 million
Paper manufacturing	not available
New investments	not available

NEWFOUNDLAND AND LABRADOR

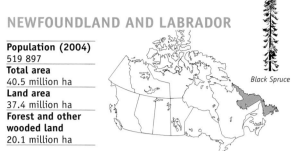

Black Spruce

Population (2004)
519 897
Total area
40.5 million ha
Land area
37.4 million ha
**Forest and other
wooded land**
20.1 million ha

FOREST RESOURCE

Ownership	
Provincial*	99%
Private	1%
Forest type	
Softwood	93%
Hardwood	1%
Mixedwood	6%
Annual allowable cut (2001)[a]	2.6 million m^3
Harvest (volume) Industrial roundwood (2002)[b]	2.1 million m^3
Harvest (area) Industrial roundwood (2002)	22 027 ha
Status of harvested Crown land (2001)[c]	
Stocked (81%)	360 000 ha
Understocked (19%)	83 000 ha
Area defoliated by insects and beetle-killed trees (2002)[d]	132 985 ha
Number of fires (2003)[e]	191
Area burned (2003)[e]	36 533 ha

FOREST INDUSTRY

Value of exports (2003)	$553.1 million
Softwood lumber	$9.0 million
Newsprint	$537.4 million
Other paper and paperboard	$6.1 million
Converted paper	$0.4 million
Other products	$0.2 million
Major export markets (2003)	$553.1 million
United States	$213.4 million
European Union	$187.3 million
South and Central America	$102.0 million
Other countries	$50.4 million
Balance of trade (2003)	$537.5 million
Value of shipments	not available
Logging	not available
Wood product manufacturing (2001)	$106.6 million
Paper manufacturing	not available
Number of establishments (2001)	not available
Logging	not available
Wood product manufacturing	72
Paper manufacturing	9
Direct employment (2003)	3 400
Wages and salaries	not available
Logging	not available
Wood product manufacturing (2001)	$19.5 million
Paper manufacturing	not available
New investments	not available

*Timber and property rights for 69% of the Crown land on the island of Newfoundland
has been conveyed to pulp and paper companies through 99 year licences issued under
the 1905 Pulp and Paper Manufacturing Act and 1935 Bowater Act. Therefore, the
Province's financial and legal system treats this licenced land as private porperty.*

YUKON

Subalpine Fir

Population (2004)
31 408
Total area
48.2 million ha
Land area
47.4 million ha
Forest and other wooded land
22.8 million ha

FOREST RESOURCE

Ownership	
Federal	100%
Forest type	
Softwood	79%
Hardwood	2%
Mixedwood	19%
Annual allowable cut (2001)[a]	267 thousand m³
Harvest (volume) Industrial roundwood (2002)[b]	7.0 thousand m³
Harvest (area) Industrial roundwood (2002)	42 ha
Status of harvested Crown land (2001)[c]	
Stocked (45%)	5 700 ha
Understocked (55%)	7 000 ha
Area defoliated by insects and beetle-killed trees[d]	not available
Number of fires (2003)[e]	77
Area burned (2003)[e]	49 037 ha

FOREST INDUSTRY

Value of exports (2003)	$579 306
Softwood lumber	$46 292
Other products	$533 014
Major export markets (2003)	$579 306
United States	$579 306
Balance of trade (2003)	$581 288

NORTHWEST TERRITORIES

Jack Pine

Population (2004)
42 321
Total area
134.6 million ha
Land area
118.3 million ha
Forest and other wooded land
33.3 million ha

FOREST RESOURCE

Ownership	
Federal	100%
Forest type	
Softwood	53%
Mixedwood	47%
Annual allowable cut[a]	not applicable
Harvest (volume) Industrial roundwood (2002)[b]	3.0 thousand m³
Harvest (area) Industrial roundwood (2002)	50 ha
Status of harvested Crown land[c]	
Stocked	not available
Understocked	not available
Area defoliated by insects and beetle-killed trees[d]	not available
Number of fires (2003)[e]	160
Area burned (2003)[e]	127 821 ha

FOREST INDUSTRY

Value of exports	not available
Major export markets	not available
Balance of trade	not available

NUNAVUT

Population (2004)
29 496
Total area
209.3 million ha
Land area
193.6 million ha
Forest and other wooded land
0.9 million ha

FOREST RESOURCE

Ownership	
Federal	100%
Forest type	
Softwood	52%
Mixedwood	48%

FOREST INDUSTRY

Value of exports (2003)	$36 756
Converted paper	$237
Other products	$36 519
Major export markets (2003)	$36 756
European Union	$28 370
Japan	$4 250
South and Central America	$3 962
Other countries	$174
Balance of trade (2003)	$37 877

28

Forestry STATISTICS

Trade Balance

Canada's trade balance (exports minus imports) was $45.7 billion in 2003. As they do every year, forest products played a major role, contributing $29.7 billion. That represents a drop of 9.6% from 2002; however, the decline in the trade balance is mainly due to the increase in the Canadian dollar relative to the U.S. dollar. Since the price of forest products sold on international markets is set in U.S. currency, when that currency weakens in relation to Canadian currency, fewer Canadian dollars are received for a sale that is expressed in U.S. dollars. In 2003 the value of sales in U.S. dollars remained much the same as in 2002, but because of the exchange rate the sales were equal to fewer Canadian dollars.

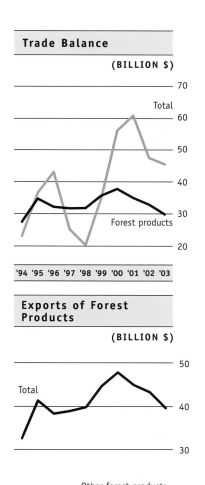

Trade Balance

(BILLION $)

2003	Billion $	Annual change (%)	
		1 year	10 years
Trade balance	45.7	-4.2	10.0
Forest products contribution	29.7	-9.6	2.9

Exports of Forest Products

The vast majority of Canada's forest product exports go to the United States. The exchange rate for Canadian dollars against U.S. dollars is therefore crucial in determining the value of exports. Since exports are sold in U.S. dollars, the higher the value of the U.S. dollar compared to the Canadian dollar, the greater will be the value of exports expressed in Canadian dollars. In 2003 the U.S. dollar declined against the Canadian dollar, so the value of exports (expressed in Canadian dollars) dropped. Canadian forest product exports amounted to $39.6 billion in 2003, down from $43.2 billion for 2002. However, if the U.S. dollar had remained as strong against the Canadian dollar as in 2002, these exports would have been worth $44.4 billion, 12% higher than the actual figure. Of the three main Canadian forest products exported—wood pulp, softwood lumber and newsprint—wood pulp best resisted the general decline in the value of exports. Unlike the other two products, wood pulp is mostly exported to countries other than the United States, and wood pulp prices were rising on international markets in 2003.

Exports of Forest Products

(BILLION $)

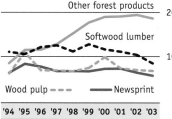

Wood pulp - - - ——Newsprint

2003	Billion $	Annual change (%)	
		1 year	10 years
Softwood lumber	8.5	-18.5	-0.8
Newsprint	5.6	-10.8	-0.7
Wood pulp	6.8	-2.9	3.9
Other forest products	18.7	-4.1	10.7
Total	**39.6**	**-8.3**	**4.0**

29

Softwood Lumber

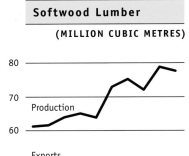

Softwood Lumber

(MILLION CUBIC METRES)

Canadian companies exporting softwood lumber to the United States have had to pay anti-dumping and countervailing duties of 27.2% since May 2002. The total cumulative value of those duties is now estimated to be $2 billion. Nevertheless, Canadian sawmills continue to export to the United States, even slightly increasing their market share. Also, there is promising news for Canadian sawmills: a North American Free Trade Agreement (NAFTA) panel of experts ruled in Canada's favour in April 2004. They judged that Canadian exports were not harming U.S. producers, and that the imposition of duties was therefore illegal. The U.S. industry is expected to appeal the NAFTA ruling; however, if the decision is upheld, not only will the 27.2% tax be removed, but Canadian sawmills may be refunded the duties paid so far. Canadian consumption of softwood lumber declined 6.6% in 2003, owing to a drop in residential repair activities.

2003	Million cubic metres	Annual change (%)	
		1 year	10 years
Production	77.6	-1.5	2.8
Exports	50.8	1.7	1.7
Consumption	27.4	-6.6	5.4

Wood Pulp

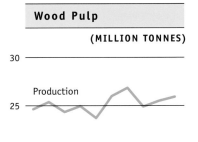

Wood Pulp

(MILLION TONNES)

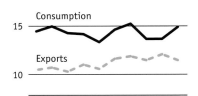

Canada is the world's second-largest producer of wood pulp. Although most of Canada's production remains in the country to manufacture paper, over 11 million tonnes were sold on the international market in 2003, making Canada the world's largest exporter of wood pulp. The price of wood pulp on international markets rose in 2003, partially offsetting a drop in the quantity exported; export revenues were thus about the same as in 2002. While exports decreased by 600 000 tonnes, consumption of pulp to produce paper rose by 1 200 000 tonnes, resulting in an increase in imports of 200 000 tonnes and a rise in production of 400 000 tonnes.

2003	Million tonnes	Annual change (%)	
		1 year	10 years
Production	25.9	1.7	1.3
Exports	11.5	-5.0	2.1
Consumption	14.9	8.9	0.8

30

Newsprint

Canada is the world's leading producer of newsprint. Because seven of every eight newsprint rolls produced in Canada are sold on international markets, it is also the largest exporter; in fact, it exports more than all other countries combined. Canadian newsprint consumption remained the same in 2003 as in the previous year, reflecting a slowdown in newsprint consumption observed for at least a decade in North America. Some newsprint machines, consequently, have been modified by Canadian producers to make other types of paper which have higher rates of consumption. These papers are better in quality and permit greater use of colour and better photograph reproduction. They are often used for advertising inserts.

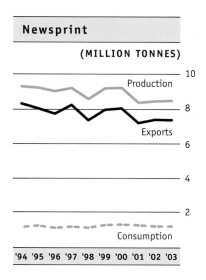

Newsprint

(MILLION TONNES)

2003	Million tonnes	Annual change (%)	
		1 year	10 years
Production	8.5	0.4	-0.7
Exports	7.4	-0.3	-0.8
Consumption	1.2	0.0	0.3

Direct Employment

Canada's forest industry gained 14 900 jobs from 2002 to 2003, for a total of 376 300 jobs, a record for the past ten years. The workforce grew in all subsectors: wood industries showed the greatest increase, with 10 450 more jobs, followed by logging with a gain of 3 100 jobs, then forestry services with 700 added jobs, and paper with 650 added jobs.

For the past ten years wood industries have continued to be the driving force for the forest industry, with an exceptional average annual growth rate of 4.7%, and a net gain of over 77 000 jobs. Job growth in logging and forestry services has been more modest (around 1% annually), and employment in paper and allied industries has declined by about 1% per year.

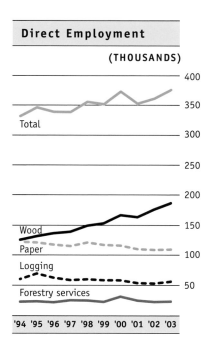

Direct Employment

(THOUSANDS)

2003	Person-years	Annual change (%)	
		1 year	10 years
Total	**376 300**	**4.1**	**1.9**
Wood product manufacturing	187 750	5.9	4.7
Paper manufacturing	109 850	0.6	-1.0
Logging	56 000	6.0	0.9
Forestry services	22 700	3.2	1.4

Capital and Repair Expenditures

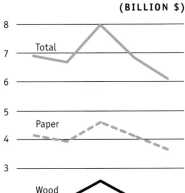

Capital and Repair Expenditures

(BILLION $)

Total

Paper

Wood

Logging

'93 '94 '95 '96 '97 '98 '99 '00 '01 '02

Capital and repair expenditures in the forest industries were only $6.1 billion in 2002, the lowest level recorded in nine years. Because of the softwood lumber dispute, since May 2002 Canada's forest industry has been required to pay anti-dumping and countervailing duties to the U.S. government, limiting their working capital and possibly their ability to obtain capital on the financial markets. It is not surprising that with the erosion of their profits by the U.S. import tariffs and the financial market instability due to the dispute, the industry limited its investments to a minimum. Although less than a year of underinvestment does not necessarily affect production capacity and competitiveness, the companies' long-term survival may be threatened if the situation persists. Thus, it is important to monitor the situation closely.

2002	Billion $	Annual change (%)	
		1 year	5 years
Total	**6.1**	**-10.8**	**-4.5**
Wood product manufacturing	1.8	-7.6	-5.3
Paper manufacturing	3.6	-11.4	-4.7
Logging	0.7	-15.7	-0.7

Maple Products

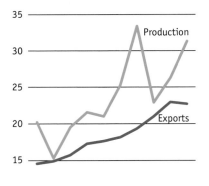

Maple Products (in syrup equivalents)

(MILLION LITRES)

Production

Exports

Consumption

'94 '95 '96 '97 '98 '99 '00 '01 '02 '03

Maple sap collection was originally a traditional cottage industry and seasonal activity. Now, however, the collection of sap, and its transformation into syrup, butter, maple taffy and maple sugar, is a prosperous and rapidly expanding industry. Producers have developed an export market that has grown at the extraordinary annual rate of 6.4% over the past decade. However, the industry is a victim of its own success: production increased at a rate of 10% per year during the same period, creating huge surpluses. Inventories are so high that it would take many years of bad harvesting to clear them. This situation could cause lower prices, and hence a decline in the industry's profitability. In 2002, the gross value of production was $155 million, compared with $149 million the previous year. Exports were valued at $147 million in 2003—a 4.5% decrease from the previous year, while the volume of exports decreased by 1.1% during the same period.

2003	Million litres	Annual change (%)	
		1 year	10 years
Production	31.3	19.2	10.0
Exports	22.7	-1.1	6.4
Consumption	6.3	-1.1	3.7 (6 years)

Christmas Trees

Christmas trees, with their wonderful scent of pine and fir, are one way for city dwellers to enjoy Canada's natural forests. Approximately 1.7 million Canadian households bought a Christmas tree in 2001, and 2.7 million Christmas trees were exported to the United States, for a total of over 4.1 million Christmas trees produced in Canada in 2001. This production is comparable to earlier years, but the destination of the trees is gradually changing. Canadian consumption, which was 2.4 million trees in 1992, is declining, while our exports are increasing. In 2001, producers had estimated revenues of nearly $70 million, including exports of close to $44 million.

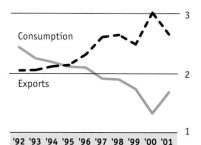

Christmas Trees

(MILLIONS)

'92 '93 '94 '95 '96 '97 '98 '99 '00 '01

2001	Millions	Annual change (%)	
		1 year	10 years
Production	4.1	0.6%	-1.2%
Exports	2.7	-11.8%	1.7%
Consumption	1.7	25.9%	-4.6%

Wildlife/Ranch-Raised Pelts

Trapping was one of the first economic activities of the New World. Today, the most expensive furs (mink and fox) come from fur farms, but approximately half still come from our forests and are harvested by trappers using traditional methods. The number of furs from fur farms has been steadily increasing since 1993, while the number from trapping fluctuates, going from 815 000 in 1992 to 1 547 000 in 1997.* In 2001, the last year for which data are available, 1.14 million furs came from fur farms and 1.01 million from trapping.* Revenues from ranch-raised fur were $50 million during this period, while those from trapping* were $23.2 million.

*Note: * Excludes sealskins*

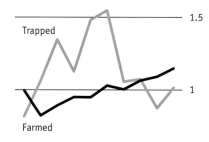

Pelts—Farmed and Trapped

(MILLION PELTS)

'92 '93 '94 '95 '96 '97 '98 '99 '00 '01

2001	Million pelts	Annual change (%)	
		1 year	10 years
Farmed	1.1	5.2%	6.3%
Trapped	1.0	16.0%	1.3%

Number of Forest Fires

(THOUSANDS)

10

8

6

'94 '95 '96 '97 '98 '99 '00 '01 '02 '03

Area Burned

(MILLION HECTARES)

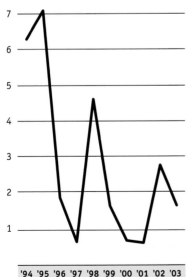

7

6

5

4

3

2

1

'94 '95 '96 '97 '98 '99 '00 '01 '02 '03

Forest Fires

Forest fires in Canada vary considerably in number and in size of forest area burned. There is a great fluctuation in fire activity both among provinces and territories in a given year and within a given province or territory over the years. For example, British Columbia went from a low of 1 876 hectares burned in 1997 to a record high of 266 412 hectares burned in 2003.

At the end of the 2003 fire season, the total number of fires was slightly above average (108%) and the total area burned was well below average (58%). Since 1994 a decreasing overall trend in the total number of fires has resulted in an average annual number of fires for this 10-year period of 7 591.

Although fires larger than 200 hectares represent a small percentage (3%) of the total number of fires, they account for 97% of the area burned. The record-setting seasons for area burned were in 1994, 1995 and 1998. New technology and research that analyzes fire and weather data, monitors fires using satellites, studies fire behaviour and models future activity will help us to better understand fire and the role it plays.

	2003	Ten-year average
Total number of fires	8 218	7 591
Total area burned	1.6 million ha	2.8 million ha

Insect Defoliation

Insect populations were relatively stable in Canada in 2002, except for the mountain pine beetle epidemic in interior British Columbia, the large aspen tortrix across Canada and the gypsy moth in eastern Canada. The mountain pine beetle, the most destructive pest of mature pine in British Columbia, continues to be one of the largest causes of economic loss and damage to environmental values in the province. Preliminary 2003 data indicate that over 4 million hectares of mountain pine beetle damage occurred. The area damaged was twice that of 2002. Spruce budworm, prevalent across the country, remains at levels well below the major infestations that occurred in the early 1990s. Forest tent caterpillar defoliation is also less severe than the devastating defoliation in the early 1990s. Although the forest tent caterpillar defoliation level for 2001 was high, only when trees are defoliated by this insect for three to four consecutive years is there a substantial impact on tree growth.

The threat from invasive alien insects and diseases is of increasing concern. In the past century, many of these species arrived from Europe and have become established, some with devastating effects on forest health. The gypsy moth, one of these invasive aliens, has established itself in the forests of eastern Canada and British Columbia and is causing damage to several hardwood species.

With an increase in global trade, Asia is now also a major source of invasive alien species. The presence of brown spruce longhorn beetle was confirmed in 2000 in Point Pleasant Park in Halifax. The Asian longhorn beetle, found in Toronto in 2003, is a growing threat to the maples of the southern hardwood forest. Similarly, emerald ash borer arrived in Canada in 2002 and is killing ashes, a major economic and aesthetic species in southwestern Ontario. Even though these three recent Asian arrivals are very localized (not included in the graph as no data are available), they still pose a threat to Canadian forests if they escape the quarantine areas.

Areas Defoliated by Four Major Insects and Beetle-Killed Trees

(MILLION HECTARES)

- - - Spruce budworm
- - - Forest tent caterpillar
—— Large aspen tortrix
—— Mountain pine beetle

15
12
9
6
3
0

'93 '94 '95 '96 '97 '98 '99 '00 '01 '02

Area Defoliated by Gypsy Moth

(THOUSAND HECTARES)

150
100
50

'93 '94 '95 '96 '97 '98 '99 '00 '01 '02

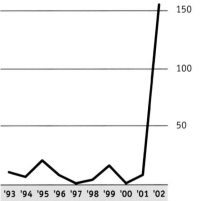

35

Potential Harvest vs. Actual Harvest of Industrial Roundwood

(MILLION CUBIC METRES)

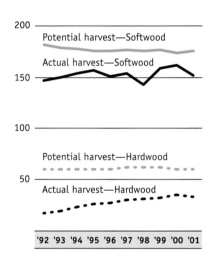

Annual Allowable Cuts and Harvests

The regulation of harvest levels is a legal requirement for licensed forest management activities on public lands. Each forest estate subject to this legislation has a certain harvest level specified for it—an Allowable Annual Cut (AAC), which is the annual level of harvest allowed over a certain period of time.

AACs are revised periodically to reflect changing conditions and improvements in knowledge. They apply to harvest on provincial lands; no legislated requirement currently applies to private, territorial or federal land tenures. The managers of these lands may have commitments to specific harvest targets, but there are no obvious (legislated) accountability mechanisms. Since the estimates presented in this graph account for private and federal lands as well as provincial Crown lands, they are referred to as "potential harvest" rather than AACs.

Canada's potential harvest has remained relatively stable since 1991. The 2001 potential harvest was 237 million cubic metres: 177 million cubic metres in softwoods and 60 million cubic metres in hardwoods. Approximately one-third of Canada's potential harvest is in British Columbia, 38% is in Quebec and Ontario, the Prairie provinces comprise roughly 19%, and the Atlantic region has 9%. The hardwood harvest has been steadily increasing over time, and more than doubled between 1991 and 2001. Softwood harvests, while variable, have remained relatively constant since peaking in 1987, averaging 151 million cubic metres over the past 10 years. This follows a number of years of significant increase (2.8% per year from 1970 to 1987).

2001	Million cubic metres	Annual change (%)	
		1 year	10 years
Potential harvest—Softwood	176.5	1.2	-0.5
Actual harvest—Softwood	151.7	-6.6	0.9
Potential harvest—Hardwood	60.3	-0.3	-0.2
Actual harvest—Hardwood	33.0	-5.4	7.7

Regeneration of Harvested Forest Land

Since the 1980s, most provinces and territories have passed laws or signed agreements requiring logging companies to ensure regeneration on sites they harvest. The graph shows the extent of successful regeneration on about 18.7 million hectares of public forest lands harvested between 1975 and 2001. Regeneration status is based on three factors: adequacy of tree cover of commercial species, density of crop (planted or seeded) trees, and the competing non-crop vegetation. Uneven-aged stands—where a tree canopy is maintained through repeated harvests—are not included in the land base shown in the graph.

The 2.5 million hectares of land unaccounted for in the graph is the area that has remained understocked—that is, that has not yet regenerated with enough trees of commercial species. These areas are not barren, having regenerated with a variety of woody and herbaceous plants, but do not yet contain sufficient trees of commercial species to be considered successfully regenerated for harvesting purposes.

Natural regeneration plays a much larger role in Canadian forestry than planting or seeding, accounting for 85% of the estimated 16.2 million hectares of forest land successfully regenerated by 2001. In recent years the area regenerated has exceeded the area harvested.

Forest Regeneration

(MILLION HECTARES)

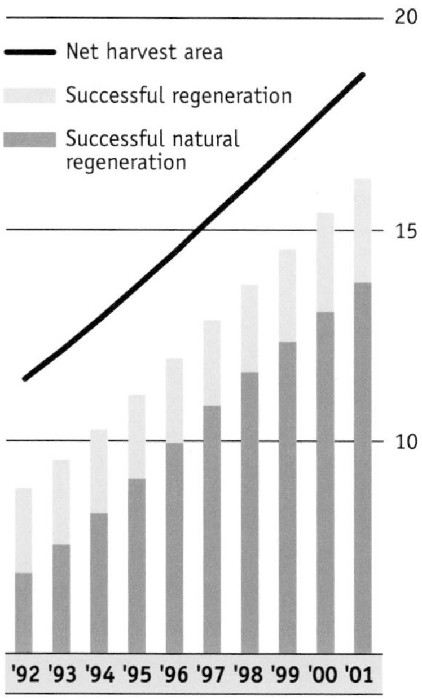

2001	Million hectares	Annual change (%)	
		1 year	10 years
Net harvest area	18.7	4.7	5.6
Successful natural regeneration	13.8	5.2	8.0
Successful planting and seeding	2.4	5.2	2.2

NOTES

Data Sources

The main sources for the data are Statistics Canada, Environment Canada, the Forest Products Association of Canada, Natural Resources Canada—Canadian Forest Service, the National Forestry Database and the Canadian Interagency Forest Fire Centre. Most of the information for the National Forestry Database was collected by provincial and territorial natural resource ministries. At the time of publication, data were preliminary. As data are finalized, they will be made available on the Internet in the National Forestry Database Program's *Compendium of Canadian Forestry Statistics* (http://nfdp.ccfm.org).

In 2000, major conceptual and methodological changes were incorporated into the Annual Survey of Manufacturers (ASM). With 2000 as reference year, the universe was expanded to cover all manufacturing units. In addition to the incorporated manufacturing businesses over $30,000 in sales of manufactured goods and with employees, the new ASM also includes: a) all incorporated businesses under $30,000 that had employees, b) all incorporated businesses that did not have any employees regardless of their annual sales value, and c) all unincorporated businesses. (Reference: CANSIM Tables 301-0003 and 301-0005 at http://cansim2.statcan.ca).

Beginning with reference year 2000, data for Head Offices are no longer included, which affects the following variables: administration employees and salaries; total employees, salaries and wages; cost of materials, supplies and goods for resale; value of shipments; and other revenue and total value added.

Forest and Other Wooded Land

The data regarding Canada's forest and other wooded land are based on Canada's Forest Inventory 2001 (Can FI 2001), which uses different categories than CanFI 1991. Comparisons between CanFI 1991 and CanFI 2001 cannot be made in a meaningful way due to a number of differences in methods and definitions in the source inventories (see text box entitled "About the CanFI 2001 Statistics" in Overview section of this report).

Land Area

Canada's total land area of 998.5 million hectares factors in all geographical features including lakes, rivers, streams and watersheds. The land area of 909.4 million hectares excludes these features.

Forest Resource

Ownership data are provided for the total forest and other wooded land.

Although the federal government maintains ownership in the Yukon and Northwest Territories, the territorial governments have responsibility for management of forests and selected other natural resources.

[a] **Annual allowable cut (AAC):** The level of harvest set by the provinces and territories for a year. AAC figures include data for both softwoods and hardwoods. The AAC figures for Newfoundland, Prince Edward Island, Nova Scotia, New Brunswick, Quebec and Manitoba include federal, provincial and private lands. Given the differences outlined below, a national AAC cannot be calculated by simply adding the provincial and territorial AACs.

- The national AAC figure was arrived at by estimating some data for private and federal lands, and converting the Ontario area figures into volume figures.

- Ontario provides figures for AAC (which it refers to as the "maximum allowable depletion") in hectares only.

- Alberta and Ontario do not include figures for private lands in their AACs.

- British Columbia does not include all private lands in its AAC.

- There are no AACs in the Northwest Territories or Nunavut.

b **Harvesting:** The national and provincial figures for harvesting volume include data for industrial roundwood only. The harvest level for fuelwood or firewood for a single province may range as high as 2.2 million cubic metres, and is not included in these harvest figures.

- Although the AAC for British Columbia does not include all private lands, these lands are included in the harvest figure. The yearly harvest rate for British Columbia may fluctuate, and in some cases it may exceed the AAC. Over a five-year period, however, the harvest figure would be equal to or lower than the AAC.

c **Status of harvested Crown land:** These data reflect the cumulative area harvested since 1975. Except for Prince Edward Island, data for private lands are not included. The term "stocked" refers to land where the forest cover meets certain timber-production standards established by forest management agencies in each province and territory. The term "understocked" refers to harvested land that requires silviculture treatments, such as site preparation, planting, seeding or weeding, to meet established standards. This category also includes land that has not yet been surveyed. A significant proportion of recently harvested areas will always be reported as understocked because of the time lag between harvesting and observable results of subsequent treatments. The small percentage of the area harvested each year that is devoted to access roads is not included in these data.

d **Insect defoliation and beetle-killed trees:** The data relating to insects were provided by provincial and territorial agencies, and they include moderate to severe defoliation only. Defoliation does not always imply mortality; for example, stands with moderate defoliation often recover and may not lose much growth. Also, defoliation is mapped on an insect species basis, and a given area may be afflicted by more than one insect at a time. This may result in double or triple counting in areas affected by more than one insect, exaggerating the extent of the total area defoliated.

e All "area burned" figures are from the Canadian Interagency Forest Fire Centre. Area burned includes areas within National Parks.

Sparking Discussion on FOREST FIRES

Imagine you have become fire chief of a major Canadian city. Your budget to protect the residents' lives and property from fire is $1 billion.

How will you put that money to best use?

You probably won't spend a billion dollars on fire trucks. You know smoke detectors keep more people safe than fire trucks. (Since 1978, house-fire deaths in Canada have decreased by about 50 percent, though our population has grown significantly. This is largely attributable to increased public awareness and more houses with smoke detectors.) Although fire trucks are necessary, they are not the complete package.

As municipal fire chief, you will divide your "eggs" into three "baskets" to address suppression, preparedness and mitigation. You will purchase an appropriate mix of equipment, organize inspections, order repairs, ensure codes and standards are in place and enforced, educate people about evacuation procedures, and work with insurance companies on issues such as building design.

In a report on Canada's forests, why talk about municipal fire protection? Because many of the concepts that apply to urban protection can be transferred to forest fire management.

Obviously, we can't hang smoke detectors on every tenth tree. But the thinking that goes into keeping cities safe applies to the forest as well.

In this edition of *The State of Canada's Forests* we consider forest fires in Canada and their positive and negative impacts. Elsewhere in this report you will find information about what is being done towards effective forest fire management. Here I will

deal with what we—the Canadian Forest Service and others involved in forest fire management— believe must be done in coming years to protect Canadians' lives and property and the environment.

We know certain things about wildfire:

- Climate change is a reality and one by-product is an increased probability of forest fires.

- Communities are expanding into the forest. Our presence there increases the risk of wildfire and therefore the risk to life, property and the forest.

- Canada is a world leader in forest fire suppression. But, as with hurricanes, floods and tornadoes, sometimes Mother Nature presents unstoppable fire conditions.

Those of us working to understand and manage forest fires must take a fresh look at recently developed knowledge, and ask some fundamental questions about how we manage fires.

The same thinking that goes into urban fire protection can be applied to forest fires. There is an emotional tug towards the rural equivalent of fire trucks—airtankers (also known as water bombers)—but suppression is expensive, especially when it involves aircraft.

Here are some quick facts, elaborated elsewhere in this report. Fire occurrence and area burned vary each year, but the annual average over the past 40 years is about 2.8 million hectares. Ninety-seven percent of forest fires are extinguished before

Brian Emmett with members of his management team.

they consume 200 hectares. The escaping three percent use up 80 percent of the nearly $1 billion spent on firefighting annually. Because of diminishing marginal returns, if resources put into firefighting were doubled, we would reduce the number of escaping fires by only 0.5 to 1.0 percent. So, regardless of the total dollars going into fire suppression, some wildfires will always escape.

Since no governments are cash-rich these days, we have to be imaginative as we investigate the best ways to manage forest fires.

We know that fire is a natural part of the ecosystem and that we will need to use more prescribed burning, but fires will still have to be suppressed and suppression will remain expensive. We will still need to explore different models for increasing efficiency and smoothing cash flow—such as leasing rather than buying airtankers.

The formula of suppression, preparedness and mitigation, used by the municipal fire chief, is appropriate for our forest fire management strategy. Suppression expenditures should ensure a modern fleet of equipment and trained personnel; develop a national training program integrating wildland and municipal suppression techniques; develop new technologies such as remote sensing to provide rapid, cost-effective wildfire information; and provide new equipment, such as external sprinkler systems that could pre-soak homes in advance of approaching fire.

We must ensure we are ready for fire's arrival in our community. Preparedness means having individual and municipal emergency response plans, evacua-

tion routes and operational suppression equipment. We also need an early warning system: fortunately, Canada's excellent fire danger rating system, used worldwide, may be the next best thing to hanging smoke detectors on trees.

Mitigation is equally important. We know that keeping city building codes up to date lessens fire damage to people and property. For forests, this means looking seriously at fire-resistant building materials and reducing flammable vegetation around homes and communities—in other words, a national FireSmart program. We must fully integrate fire into land and resource management, and use forest management activities, such as harvesting, silviculture, road layout and prescribed burning, to reduce the potential for unwanted wildfires.

A broader, more integrated view of forest fires will allow us to be more cost-efficient. We should look at pooling risk—the underlying concept in insurance. Our strategy must reflect fire dynamics and make good business sense, so taxpayers can understand how we are dealing with this challenge. A fire-smart, business-smart system will more efficiently and effectively protect life, property and the environment.

At the CFS, we understand data gathering and we understand the impacts. We will continue to share our knowledge and ideas with fire management agencies to develop approaches that enhance the security of Canadians and our forests' sustainability. I am sure that, reading this report, you will gain a better appreciation of the present and future challenges we all face.

Brian Emmett,
Assistant Deputy Minister, Canadian Forest Service

41

FEATURE Articles

CANADIAN SUMMERS traditionally add a new dimension to evening newscasts and morning papers: the **FOREST FIRE REPORT.** Often, viewers and readers take the briefest of notice, then turn to items of more immediate interest.

But the **SUMMER OF 2003** pushed the forest fire story to the **TOP OF THE NEWS HOUR** and thrust it onto the **FRONT PAGES OF NEWSPAPERS** at home and abroad. At the height of the drama, television viewers waited anxiously for updates about conflagrations that, for a while, seemed **UNSTOPPABLE**.

2003: THE YEAR OF THE INFERNO

We saw and read about homeowners in several communities abandoning their dwellings as they fled from the advancing flames. It seemed inevitable that whole towns would be destroyed. We watched firefighters battling day after day, becoming exhausted yet still soldiering on. We read about acts of heroism and tales of loss and devastation.

The forest fires of 2003, especially in British Columbia and Alberta, captured the public's attention, not just because there were so many of them, but because they literally hit us where we live. If these fires had consumed the same number of hectares in a remote wilderness area, the stories might have held only passing interest.

But 2003 was a catastrophic year for British Columbia, where over a quarter of a million hectares of forest were burned—more than 10 times the norm. This represented a third more wildland fires last summer as the 10-year average—the yardstick used to compare fire statistics.

What made the B.C. situation particularly tragic was that tens of thousands of residents living in the worst-hit areas had to be evacuated and close to 250 homes were destroyed in the city of Kelowna. The village of Louis Creek, north of Kamloops, was all but eradicated.

In Alberta, the residents of the community of Blairmore had to be evacuated last summer during the Lost Creek wildfire in the Crow's Nest Pass. The number of fires in Alberta was up by 24 percent. However, the area burned in 2003 was less than a

PROVINCE	NUMBER OF FIRES		AREA BURNED (HECTARES)	
	2003	**10-year average**	**2003**	**10-year average**
British Columbia	2 447	1 803	266 412	19 168
Alberta	1 191	963	55 482	191 131
Manitoba	1 148	502	430 170	339 786
Ontario	1 015	1 341	314 219	196 403
Canada	**8 218**	**7 591**	**1 636 764**	**2 811 326**

third of the average. Manitoba was also hard hit in 2003, with more than twice the usual number of forest fires and slightly over the usual area burned. While Ontario actually had fewer fires than the norm, the area burned increased by about a third.

Still, according to the National Forest Fire Report issued by the Canadian Forest Service, while the number of forest fires reported across Canada in 2003 exceeded the average by 627, the 1.64 million hectares burned was actually down by more than one million hectares from the 10-year national average.

The two feature articles that follow will explore in detail the reasons and causes for forest fires, their consequences, and what is being done to prevent or control them.

The Nature of **FOREST**
FIRES

FIRE IN THE FOREST

Canada's boreal forest is a vast tract of mainly coniferous woodland that stretches over 1000 kilometres between the frozen Arctic and the more temperate forests and grasslands to the south. Every summer, some part of these woodlands will turn into a raging inferno.

This particular area of Canada's boreal forest, made up mostly of pine, spruce and other evergreens, has been hot and dry for the better part of a week. It's difficult to view the surroundings because the crowns of the mature trees have formed a tight canopy that allows only the occasional sunbeam to penetrate. Underfoot, there is a multi-season accumulation of needles, twigs and fallen branchlets, referred to by foresters as the duff layer. The recent dry weather has turned this accumulation into a carpet of potential kindling. A slight breeze riffles through the moisture-depleted needles of the tall conifers, causing a restless tremor, as if the trees sense that something is about to happen.

Perhaps it's a live match tossed aside by a careless hiker after lighting a cigarette. Or the embers of a hastily extinguished, abandoned camp-fire scattered onto the tinder-dry forest floor by a wayward gust of wind. Or repeated lightning strikes from an overhead stack-up of storm clouds formed as a result of the hot, dry weather.

Whatever the cause, a small patch of forest begins to smoulder and, because of the readily available tinder, soon bursts into flame. It is primed to become one of about 10 000 forest fires that will have an impact on an estimated 2.5 to 3 million hectares of forest in Canada in any given year.

How much terrain this particular wildfire will engulf depends on numerous factors, such as how quickly it's spotted, whether it's in an area easily accessible to firefighting equipment, the local fire management policies, the current weather conditions, the amount of combustible vegetation on site, and the surrounding topography. In addition, whether it's in an area deemed high- or low-risk to humans and property, and how rich it is in commercial timber resources, will affect whether the experts quickly suppress it or allow it to burn out on its own (while being monitored).

These factors will be explored as we consider the history of wildland fires in Canada, the conditions that lead to forest fires, and the ecological, economic and social consequences they bring.

45

IN TIMES GONE BY

UNTIL the coming of the European settlers, Canada's forests thrived on nature's pattern of control—arboreal life cycles that revolved mainly around insect infestations, disease, and fires caused by lightning or those deliberately set by Aboriginal peoples.

Aboriginal peoples in various parts of the country set fires for several reasons: to clear the forest for crop lands that provided food and medicinal plants, to manage wildlife habitat, and to give themselves living space. Burning was done at specific times of the year and under weather conditions that allowed flames to be contained within a designated area. Such an undertaking, called "prescribed burning" in Canada and "fire use" in certain other forested countries, required special knowledge and skills in fire behaviour and vegetation reaction—skills that for the most part became lost when the native peoples' way of life changed drastically in the nineteenth century.

In pre-settler days, the normal routine was to treat specific areas with fire on a four- or five-year cycle (although certain noxious plants were burned more frequently). This rotational burning provided Aboriginal harvesters with a landscape area large enough to grow crops. These native peoples used low-intensity fires that enriched the nutrients in the soil, allowing many medicinal plants to flourish in the burned-over areas.

The fire season in Canada began in April, when grass fires scorched the landscape. A flurry of spring fires after the snow melt was followed by a decline, as deciduous and coniferous stands greened up, producing a new growth of moisture-laden, fire-resistant leaves and needles. Hot, dry summer weather brought on wildfires sparked by lightning and Aboriginal-controlled burn-offs. Then fires decreased and eventually stopped with the onset of wet fall weather.

Although in pre-settler days fire regularly burned large sections of Canada's boreal forest, robust new trees quickly emerged to replace the consumed timber. Over the millennia, much of the vegetation became fire-dependent, actually requiring regular fire cycles for renewal.

Lodgepole and jack pine, for instance, developed resin-sealed cones—termed serotinous—that stay on trees for many years. With the heat of a forest fire, the resin melts and the cones pop open, scattering seeds that within 15 years or so can produce new forest growth. Plants that have fire-adapted traits use whatever means are available to perpetuate the species. Certain tree types such as the Ponderosa pine and Douglas fir have thicker bark that resists fire damage and nurtures tender shoots within.

46

Others, such as the trembling aspen, use the soil as insulation for post-fire recovery through a network of suckers (underground roots) that quickly sprout in the nutrient-rich soil resulting from a fire.

Nature also had a pattern of fire activity, or fire regime, which was different for every region in Canada. Each fire regime has its own length of fire intervals (years between fires on one site), average area burned annually and fire severity. In a country as vast as ours, fires of varying intensities can occur as often as every 10 or 15 years in some grassland areas or as rarely as once in well over 500 years in the moisture-laden old-growth areas of the west coast. The average interval between fires in our boreal forest before the arrival of the European settlers has been estimated at 75 to 100 years. A fire regime integrates many natural and cultural influences. It changes only with significant shifts in climate or in fire policies, or when humans profoundly alter the fuel structure. All three of these changes have come into play since the European settlement of Canada.

FIRE: FRIEND OR FOE?

AT FIRST, the European newcomers saw the forest itself as the enemy, an obstacle that had to be cleared by various means (including burning) in order to build communities and open up areas to agriculture. Mining entrepreneurs found it much easier to locate ore deposits if the forest overstorey (the uppermost layer of foliage forming the forest canopy) was first burned off. Railroad builders regarded fire as a much easier and less expensive way to clear trackbeds than having to pay workers with saws, axes, dynamite and teams of horses to uproot and haul away the forest cover.

Once established on the land, however, these settlers reverted to their abhorrence of fire, brought with them from Europe along with their treasured possessions and cultural beliefs, as the destroyer of lives, personal property and commercial enterprises.

As the settlers pushed west and north, the feeling that the country's forests were infinite, and therefore available to be used as they saw fit, was gradually replaced by the panicky conviction that the country's great forests, rich with harvestable timber, were at risk of being wiped out by wildfires.

As the country developed, isolated settlements became dependent on the forests for both their sustenance and their livelihood. And it was soon discovered that forest-related employment could go beyond logging. There were recreational activities that the hinterland dweller not only could enjoy personally, but could offer for a fee to hikers, hunters, fishers, canoeists, bird watchers and other nature lovers.

47

SUPPRESSION AT ALL COSTS

ONCE THE NEW CANADIANS realized that forest fires could mean huge losses of human life, property and natural resources, they began to pressure law and policy makers to prevent or eradicate every wildfire within reach. All-out war was declared. Even the terminology took on combative overtones: fire fighting, water bombing, first strike, initial attack, mopping up. This is hardly surprising since many of the professional fire-fighters were veterans of real wars in Europe and elsewhere—including those "firebirds" who fought this forest-destroying enemy from the air.

The forest's potential for providing non-timber commercial products was also soon recognized. These included wildland meat and fish for domestic and export sales, other edible products such as maple syrup, berries, nuts and mushrooms, the fur and hides of various indigenous animals in demand by the fashion industry, decorative plants such as Christmas trees and floral accessories, and arts and crafts supplies. There were also—as the country's Aboriginal people had known for centuries—herbs, roots and medicinal plants with a growing market in Canada and abroad.

This groundswell of negative opinion about fire in the forest was fed from time to time by reports of catastrophic fires that destroyed communities across North America. A century of calamitous fires in Canada between 1825 and 1922 strengthened the belief that fire threatened public safety and laid waste accessible timber and non-timber products. Early foresters and the general public began to focus their efforts—at least in the southern, heavily populated areas of the country—almost exclusively on wildfire prevention and suppression.

As an era of advocacy developed, environmental groups began

lobbying to conserve mature and old-growth forests, partly through the elimination of forest fires. This insistence on so many fronts on preventing or eradicating as many forest fires as possible was fortified by technological advances in transportation, firefighting equipment, communications and, more recently, satellite and computer technology.

In recent decades, fire suppression programs have become extremely effective: about 97 percent of fires in Canada's commercial forests are contained at less than 200 hectares. The other 3 percent are difficult to control; they account for almost all of the area burned and represent most fire management expenditures in Canada. This does not include fires in extremely remote areas that are allowed to burn out on their own if they do not endanger human life or property. The timber in these areas is usually considered not commercially viable.

Ironically, however, by tampering with the natural fire cycles—and by embracing fire eradication as the overriding principle of fire management—people have set the stage for more catastrophic fires.

When certain natural fire cycles were interrupted, jack pine and other serotinous and semi-seroti-

nous conifer stands began to die off without spreading the next generation of fire-activated seedlings. This resulted in a glut of debris from dead trees and opened up the area to such species as balsam fir, which is susceptible to insect infestations that kill the trees, resulting in further flammability.

In the boreal forest, nature's way provided a mosaic pattern of fire-ravaged stands of same-age trees, creating a natural firebreak. Interfering with nature through suppression of fire in these stands set in motion the mechanism for larger, wider-ranging and often devastating blazes.

Fire management experts point out that such outbreaks release large amounts of carbon stored in both living vegetation and trunks of fallen trees. Carbon is one of the main villains in the global warming scenario, and releasing it can lead to even more disastrous fires in our wildlands. The Forest Fire Science and Technology division of the Ontario

Ministry of Natural Resources has observed a doubling each decade for the past 40 years of the number of days per month during fire season that conditions are conducive to the outbreak of devastating fires. The agency also reports that warming trends have pushed the start-times for fires to earlier dates in the spring and the stand-down times, when fire is no longer a threat, to later dates in the fall.

Various fire experts had warned of the possibility of more intense and dangerous wildfires, in both Canada and the United States, for many years. Those words of caution went largely unheeded, however, as decision makers continued to insist on lengthening intervals between fires through aggressive suppression. And many homesteaders build substantial dwellings in the wildland/ urban "interface" without using fire-retardant materials or leaving firebreaks around their property.

Fortunately, the pendulum of Canadian public opinion has begun to swing back, and many decision makers realize that not only is it impossible to extinguish every fire, it is economically unfeasible and ecologically unsound.

49

Furthermore, fire suppression is subject to the law of diminishing returns. Based on recent experiences in Canada and other developed nations, suppression seems to be reaching its limit of economic and physical effectiveness. As a research scientist at the Canadian Forest Service of Natural Resources Canada puts it: "To be able to suppress the last 3 percent of fires that cause 97 percent of the damage, we would need a firefighter behind every tree and a helicopter on every mountain slope."

Perhaps it is time to step back, study the situation from every possible angle, and come up with solutions that, while not perfect, will make the best of the situation.

FACTORS INFLUENCING FIRES

AS WE SAW in the fire scenario opening this article, many factors influence fire in our forests. The six most important are weather (widely considered the most pertinent), fuel, insect and disease infestations, an ignition source, topography and human intervention.

WEATHER

Weather has a pervasive effect on the incidence of wildfire. Catastrophic fires occur in our forests only in the warmer months, when the country is free of ice, snow and spring/autumn rains. Weather also plays a role in fuel availability: fuel sources have to be dry to burn. Weather conditions influence the ignition of fires by lightning. Furthermore, the weather can create drought conditions that turn trees to tinder and the forest floor into a carpet of combustibility. Drought and lightning strikes can also leave the vegetation open to infestations of parasitic insects and disease, which, in nature's vicious circle, create more fuel for the next flare-up.

FUEL

It's a given that if you do not have fuel, you do not have fire. The bigger the fuel load, the more intense the fire. Under natural conditions Canada's forests had settled down to an age-old cycle of limited burn, regeneration, a healthy growth period, limited burn, regeneration, and so on. Vegetation adapted to this routine and all was well with the forest. But once humans interfered with this cycle, even though there were fewer fires, the fuel load increased, inviting disaster.

INSECTS AND DISEASES

One positive effect of fire is that it regularly clears the landscape of aging trees before they become susceptible to insect infestation and disease. By suppressing as many forest fires as possible, humankind has interrupted this natural cycle,

50

allowing trees to live longer and thus become vulnerable to parasitic attack. This creates a larger and more widespread fuel load, setting the conditions for bigger, more intense fires. In addition, global trading has brought an invasion of exotic pests to prey on trees that have no natural defences against them.

IGNITION

There are two sources of ignition in our forest—lightning and humans. Lightning strikes cause nearly 40 percent of our wildfires and about 85 percent of the total area burned, because most occur in remote areas, where as many as 400 strikes can occur during a single storm.

Fires set by humans are usually located in more accessible areas, so they are easier to reach with firefighting equipment but are likely to put people and property at risk. Human-made fires are caused by careless smoking or camping, vehicles running hot in dry grass or bush, badly tended land-clearing and slash burning, downed power lines, industrial accidents (such as welding sparks), or arson.

TOPOGRAPHY

Some areas of Canada have minimal to non-existent risk of forest fires—such as the far northern lands that are under ice and snow most of the year and contain little flammable vegetation, and the west-coast rainforests where inter-

vals between fires can well exceed 500 years. On our east coast rain conditions frequently keep the land too wet for the intrusion of fire. In vast prairie areas, grassland fires are the biggest danger. In southern deciduous woodlands, fires are a definite risk, but dead leaves are less combustible than conifer needles, and they tend to trap moisture on the forest floor. Deciduous trees, moreover, do not have the high levels of combustible resins that conifers have.

It is the boreal forest in near north and western sections of Canada, with its multitudinous coniferous trees, that feeds a forest fire. And it's the rugged topography, from the dwarfed mountains of the Pre-Cambrian Shield to the lofty Rockies and other western ranges, that adds to a fire's intensity. Flames driven by high winds move uphill more rapidly than on flatlands. But nature has her own suppression techniques: rivers and mountain ridges act as natural firebreaks, and rainfall checks or extinguishes fire.

Topography can also influence rainfall, as in last year's Okanagan fires. The main victims were populated areas between two mountain ranges where rain is less frequent. After a four-year drought, the tinder-dry terrain was a tragedy waiting to happen.

51

HUMAN INTERVENTION

Containment is both the human-made and the natural way to control fire. Start a blaze in your fireplace and it will die out once it has used up the available fuel. If you want it to continue burning, you add more logs, but you still limit the quantity, and you know the boundaries of the fireplace will control the flames. If you are careless, however, you might throw a bunch of wood on the fire and settle in for a long winter's nap, with the firescreen open and a pile of kindling within a spark's jump in front of the fireplace.

This scenario is a microcosm of what humankind has done in our forests. Nature had set up a pattern of containment: at random intervals either a surface fire would clear the understorey of a stand of timber or a full-blown crown fire (boosted into the treetops by winds or a thick, dry duff layer) would take out most or all of the stand, with the fire eventually dying out due to less conducive weather conditions or a lack of fuel. Humans, by interfering with nature and interrupting this natural fire cycle, have literally added fuel to the fire. And by ignoring the warnings of fire experts, we have figuratively pulled the blankets up over our heads and gone to sleep.

52

CONSEQUENCES OF FOREST FIRES

THE CONSEQUENCES of forest fires fall into three broad categories: ecological, social and economic. As with most things in life, the consequences are not all good or all bad. One's view of a particular effect is influenced by such factors as personal loss or gain and one's own values.

ECOLOGICAL

As we have seen, fire has a beneficial influence on species composition, abundance and age. For our boreal forest, periodic cleansing through understorey burn-off and setting a mosaic of natural firebreaks will trigger new growth, clear out a flammable duff layer, and stagger the age range of vegetation to encourage regeneration.

Animal life is not unduly affected by fire. The public perception that forest fires kill vast numbers of wild animals is not correct; like the vegetation itself, animals have learned to adapt to periodic blazes.

Regular forest fires are useful to cleanse the woodlands of parasitic insects and disease. However, should the insects or disease get there first, they can create dead

shells of trees that provide even more fuel, causing larger and more destructive fires.

Forest fires can dramatically affect Canada's greenhouse gas emissions. In a year when many fires are burning, the amount of carbon released into the atmosphere can virtually equal the level emitted by industrial operations. This can affect whether Canada in a given year is considered a carbon sink (a repository of carbon) or a carbon source (when carbon escapes into the atmosphere, it helps to create greenhouse gases and speed subsequent global warming). At stake is our ability to honour our commitments under the Kyoto Accord to reduce such emissions.

Smoke and pollution also have to be considered. Smoke in communities can cause breathing problems, especially among the very young and the very old. In some cases, too much smoke leads to evacuation of the residents, with all its attendant problems. Smoke can also obscure highways in forested areas, causing traffic delays and accidents. And smoke may contribute to global warming: researchers are studying the effects of sunlight on particles of ash in smoke. Finally, smoke from fires in Canada has

53

occasionally drifted into the United States and resulted in communities infringing Environmental Protection Agency regulations, potentially causing international ill will.

Fire ecologists point out one other negative consequence of forest fires—the tragedy of a blaze destroying a rare type of habitat set aside as a park for endangered species.

SOCIAL

The social consequences of forest fires in Canada are far-reaching, from the disruptions of the normal living patterns of firefighters and community residents to health concerns related to smoke inhalation.

Evacuating residents from a fire-threatened area can have both financial and cultural costs. For native peoples, being flown to larger communities can be a particular wrench to their way of living, with the resultant exposure to such detrimental influences as fast foods, traffic hazards and an alien lifestyle.

A particularly devastating fire can result in the psychological damage of losing a home and family treasures and having to start all over again. A loss of heritage can also occur, should community halls, libraries and other structures be destroyed.

In addition, parks and recreational areas are liable to go up in smoke, creating a sense of emotional loss. In the Okanagan fires of last summer, many of the wooden railway bridges over the Kettle River were destroyed, resulting in an aesthetic loss to history buffs and a loss of convenience to hikers who used the abandoned bridges. Fortunately, these bridges are being rebuilt, but their historic value can never be recaptured.

ECONOMIC

Forest fires have consequences on both sides of the economic ledger. The loss of revenue from burned trees may not be critical, since about half the timber burned is non-commercial, located in the far north. Moreover, the loss of marketable timber could be mitigated if provincial and territorial agencies put in place measures permitting the salvaging of wood from burned-out areas. In addition, forest companies often control such large tracts of timberland that they can shift operations to another part of the forest and come back to the burned-over area once it has regenerated.

On the other hand, planning to cut in one area is expensive in itself; shifting crews and equipment to a different location increases the costs considerably. There are also potential losses of shareholder equity if the fire destroys sawmills or other property and equipment.

Although firefighting represents a huge investment by government agencies and the private sector, in training and salaries for personnel as well as purchasing and maintaining equipment, the argument can also be made that this is a normal part of doing business. In addition, many rural communities rely on the jobs provided to firefighting crews, and the Canadian economy benefits from the manufacture and sale of suppression equipment—from aircraft to pumps to hoses—both nationally and internationally.

The costs for direct fire suppression in Canada have been averaging about $500 million a year. This figure spiked in 2003, when British Columbia alone spent approximately $600 million and several other provinces had worse than normal fire seasons. While this certainly drains the public coffers, much of this money goes towards salaries, food and equipment purchases for the firefighters and buying or leasing of firefighting equipment from Canadian firms.

The cost of cleaning up and re-building in communities harmed by forest fires, while a burden to those sustaining the losses, is also a source of revenue for individuals and commercial enterprises engaged in the restorative work.

In spite of these moderating factors on monetary expenses, however, the costs in human suffering, wasted resources and devastated landscape are still considered unacceptably onerous by the over-whelming majority of forest stake-holders. Measures need to be—and are being—taken to substantially reduce these costs while safeguarding wildland sustainability through sound forest management.

WHERE DO WE GO FROM HERE?

FIRE MANAGEMENT, then, is a complex issue. Like every other element in nature, fire has both a positive and a negative side. Seeing it as a terrifying enemy to be subdued at all costs has not worked, but returning to nature's fire regimes is also no longer practical.

Kelvin Hirsch, Research Man-agement Advisor with the Canadian Forest Service's Northern Forestry Centre, Natural Resources Canada, has written: "Fire has been and is likely to become an even more significant disturbance in Canada's forest ecosystems. This means the sustainable management of these forests will be dependent upon the ability to balance the social, economic, and ecological impacts of fire. It is the responsi-bility of government, industry, non-governmental organizations, and the public to encourage and foster the open and informed evaluation and debate of the future directions of forest fire management policies and practices in Canada."

Simply put, we as forest stakehold-ers must acknowledge and accept that fire will occur, and we must learn how to live with and adapt to this fact of life.

Managing **FOREST FIRES**

THE PATH TO SUSTAINABILITY

For generations, the goal of forest fire suppression in Canada was based on a European model: fire was seen as bad and had to be prevented and controlled. Today, however, we understand that fire is a natural disturbance in forest ecosystems—a process that should be managed. A holistic approach to forest fire management considers that forest fires are integral to the health, structure and diversity of forest ecosystems. Foresters also increasingly recognize that small controlled fires result in new growth in the forests and reduce the likelihood of large, disastrous fires.

However, fires cannot be allowed to run their natural course when they threaten lives, property or resources. Canada has two levels of fire management—intensive and extensive. In the intensive zone, which includes communities, valuable timber and other values at risk, all fires are actively suppressed. In the extensive zone, forest fires are monitored and if they pose a threat to social or resource values, they may be suppressed. The key is to balance the costs and benefits of fire to help ensure the ecological, economic and social sustainability of our forests, the forest industry and forest-based communities.

FIRE MANAGEMENT IN CANADA

Fire management involves planning, preventing and fighting fires to protect people, property and the forest resource as well as using fire to attain forestry, wildlife and land-use objectives. Fire management takes place in the context of balancing environmental, social and economic criteria.

Ninety-three percent of Canada's forests are publicly owned. Therefore, fire management is largely the responsibility of provincial and territorial governments, with federal departments managing their own lands. Collectively, Canadian agencies spend between $400 million and $800 million a year on fire

management, making this one of the most costly aspects of forest management in Canada.

The Canadian Interagency Forest Fire Centre coordinates the exchange of firefighters, equipment and know-how among Canadian fire management agencies (see text box on page 64). It also compiles national forest fire statistics and facilitates information sharing among fire agencies.

Fire research in Canada involves a partnership between provincial and territorial agencies, the federal government, universities and the private sector. Scientists from across the country work together to better understand and manage forest fires.

Canada is a leading-edge nation in forest fire research; many Canadian discoveries and developments are used throughout the world.

The forest fire research program at the Canadian Forest Service (CFS), Natural Resources Canada, has evolved along with fire management. The CFS research program provides stability and continuity for the research activities carried out by industry, universities and provincial/territorial agencies.

KNOWING THE RISK

Predicting when and where a fire is most likely to start and how it will behave is the first step in suppression. Timely information

57

allows fire managers to have their equipment ready where it is most likely to be needed. A number of information systems and technologies have been developed to monitor forest and weather conditions and other factors, and provide a threat rating of fire potential.

The CFS, in cooperation with provincial and territorial fire agencies, developed the Canadian Forest Fire Danger Rating System (CFFDRS), which determines the potential risk of wildfires. The system uses weather, fuels and topography to predict fuel moisture and the likelihood of a fire starting. It also predicts the rate and direction of fire spread, fire intensity, the amount of fuel consumed, and the fire perimeter and area.

The Spatial Fire Management System (SFMS) combines the CFFDRS and fire management models in a geographic information system mapping environment. SMFS also integrates snow cover, greenup, grass curing and rainfall derived from satellite imagery or other sources. It predicts fire occurrence, models fire growth and recommends resource allocation. SFMS generates daily or hourly maps of weather conditions, fuel moisture estimates, fire ignition probability, and predicted fuel consumption, fire size and difficulty of control.

The SFMS also provides information for policy setting and review, and fire planning, such as establishing initial attack bases and weather stations. SFMS is currently used by the CFS as well as

fire agencies in British Columbia, Alberta, Saskatchewan, Yukon, Malaysia, Indonesia, New Zealand and Mexico.

Locating actual fires, monitoring their spread and observing their behaviour are crucial to fire management. Not knowing that a fire exists until it is large, or underestimating its rate of spread, could have disastrous results. Remote sensing technologies, computer modelling and Internet communication have advanced our ability to monitor fire activity in near real time, allowing agencies to manage complex fire situations more effectively.

In Quebec, lightning accounts for 25 percent of forest fires but 84 percent of area burned. All lightning strikes that hit the ground are analyzed by a computer system— Système d'Information sur les Incendies de Forêt. The system provides constant access to the most recent information on weather, fires, resources and operating costs. It also analyzes drought, fuels and fire behaviour to identify the sectors where the risk of fire is highest.

The Ontario Ministry of Natural Resources is working on a computer model—the Level of Protection Analysis Tool—that uses historic

58

weather and fire data to help managers determine the most cost-effective resources and organization to use.

THE NATIONAL SITUATION

The Canadian Wildland Fire Information System (CWFIS) is a national version of the SFMS. It automatically accesses weather data across Canada, produces daily national maps of fire weather and fire behaviour potential, and disseminates the maps through the Web. The system supports agency-level fire management decisions and national mobilization of resources, and provides a national overview of the fire situation to governments, fire agencies, the media and the public.

The Fire Monitoring, Mapping and Modelling System (FireM3) uses satellite imagery to produce daily national maps of large forest fires. A joint venture of the CFS and the Canada Centre for Remote Sensing, the system identifies and locates actively burning fires, maps the area burned, and models burning conditions and fire behaviour. Forest companies, environmental scientists and other researchers are also using this methodology to evaluate the role and impact of fire on forest ecosystems.

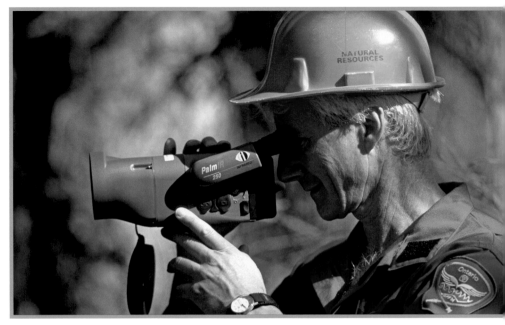

ASSESSING FIRE IMPACTS

Sustainable forest management requires assessing the impacts of wildfire on timber supply, recreational opportunities and wildlife habitat, as well as measuring the effects of various practices on fire activity. The Wildfire Threat Rating System (WTRS) combines forest data, values and management options to generate a wildfire planning model. It assesses four main components of risk: ignition, values at risk, suppression capability and expected fire behaviour. The system maps them separately and in combination to generate an overall fire-threat rating.

The WTRS helps forest managers determine how land-use decisions affect the wildfire threat in a given area. It also allows them to evaluate shifts in harvesting and silviculture, and to identify the best locations for initial attack and prescribed burning. The WTRS will be integrated into the Spatial Fire Management System to enhance the applicability of both systems.

Alberta's Sustainable Resource Development Department is developing Prometheus—a fire-growth model that automates many of the manual calculations when using the CFFDRS. It incorporates large fires jumping across or spotting ahead of a control line. This state-of-the-art model predicts the growth of large fires that have escaped initial attack; evaluates the threat of wildfires to communities, recreational facilities and other values-at-risk; and measures how

59

The British Columbia Forest Service Protection Program is using space technology to help fight forest fires. REMSAT II (Real-time Emergency Management via Satellites) provides real-time satellite data for fire management planning, firefighting and post-fire damage assessment. The system improves the flow of information across three levels of fire management—headquarters, a mobile command centre near the fire, and on-the-ground firefighters. The system identifies the positions of all the resources and equipment by navigation satellites and relays this information automatically via telecommunication satellites.

LOW-TECH WORKS TOO

A major challenge in firefighting is quickly getting a lot of water to a fire. This is particularly important at the wildland/urban interface— where homes and communities are within or on the edge of a forest. Sprinkler systems are highly effective if they are in place long enough before a fire arrives to saturate the structures and nearby fuels, and to raise the local relative humidity. Because they are installed before the fire arrives, no lives are put at risk. Also, sprinklers soak the surface without exposing the mineral soil. This is more environmentally

different strategies could affect fire behaviour. It can be used by fire agencies across Canada as well as by researchers and municipal planners to study and reduce the threat of large fires.

FIRE SUPPRESSION

Every year about 8500 forest fires are reported in Canada. Almost all of these—97 percent—are controlled at a very small size, thanks primarily to sophisticated equipment and technology, advanced research, highly trained personnel and good communications.

Canada, along with the United States and Australia, is considered very effective at suppressing fires. All three countries have excellent systems for planning, monitoring fire danger and rapidly moving resources to trouble spots. They operate on the basis that the best time to fight a fire is when it is small. Efforts are continuing to reduce the few fires that escape initial attack. These fires can cause devastating damage and become extremely difficult to control. They endanger people, property and the forest resource.

friendly than building a fire line using heavy machinery to scrape away surface material down to the mineral soil, and it reduces the chance of erosion or of silt filtering into streams or ponds.

A powerful sprinkler system, developed by Saskatchewan Environment and Sands Dragline Systems—called a Values Protection Unit—can be a powerful ally in protecting homes and other buildings. It is a high-capacity version of the sprinkler units long used by Saskatchewan firefighters, and the only one of its kind in North America.

The sprinkler system proved itself in the summer of 2003 when the Tokumm Creek fire threatened the Lake Louise and Banff areas. A Saskatchewan team laid hoses and sprinklers across the two-and-a-half-kilometre Vermillion Pass leading into the Bow River Valley

and another one and a half kilometres around the Marble Canyon Recreation Site. Pumps and sprinklers soaked a wide line across the valley and around the recreation site, allowing a back burn that stopped the fire.

PRESCRIBED BURNING

Canada has had remarkable success in putting out forest fires. Successful suppression, however, can be a two-edged sword. Fires are part of nature's way of shaping, maintaining and renewing forests. Thwarting this natural process can change the structure of tree stands, reduce forest health, lead to loss of productivity and, ironically, increase potential fire severity by allowing fuels to increase.

A key factor in the severity of a forest fire is the amount of fuel (trees, brush and surface litter)

available to burn. "Ladder fuels," in the form of low branches, young trees and other vegetation, provide "rungs" for the fire to climb to the tree crowns where the wind can rapidly spread the fire. Decades of increasingly effective fire suppression have led to a buildup of forest fuels, which increases the risk of fires, especially during hot, dry, windy weather. The severe fires that result can degrade water quality, the position of the water table and stream-flow regimes. They also release large amounts of particulates and carbon dioxide into the atmosphere.

Fire agencies are turning to prescribed burning as a way to mitigate these dangers. Fire managers can determine when a particular area is overdue for fire and trained specialists can light a prescribed fire when burning conditions are low to moderate. Such fires are carefully controlled, taking into account weather, vegetation, fire behaviour and terrain. While some risk is involved, it is much less than the risk of letting a wildfire burn unchecked or trying to exclude all fires. The cost—an average $80 per hectare—is orders of magnitude less than the millions of dollars spent fighting a large wildfire.

61

Parks Canada has played a lead role in using prescribed burning as a forest management tool. Fire managers have a dual role: providing fire protection and sustaining fire-dependent ecosystems. In the latter role, they follow a fairly aggressive program of prescribed burning. Trained staff use aerial ignition, with helicopter-mounted drip torches or chemical incendiaries for larger burns, and hand-held or truck-mounted torches to ignite roadside fuel accumulations.

Even urban forests can benefit from prescribed burns. Windsor, Ontario, uses this technique regularly in its nature preserve parks, and Toronto began regular prescribed burns in High Park, in the vicinity of prime downtown real estate, in 1997.

FIRE AND SUSTAINABLE FORESTRY

The University of Alberta's Sustainable Forest Management Network (SFMN) is one of 18 Centres of Excellence across Canada. A key part of its program is studying how natural disturbances such as fire, disease, insect infestations and human activities maintain or interfere with a forest's ecological balance. In groundbreaking work it calibrated existing infrared satellite technology to accurately find unburned islands of trees left behind in large forest fires. The work sets a baseline for analyzing the loca-

tions and distributions of unburned islands of trees using future high-resolution satellite images.

SFMN's researchers discovered that recently burned trees should be left to protect the prime feeding and nesting habitat of the three-toed and the black-backed woodpeckers. These birds migrate long distances to take advantage of the insect and beetle larvae that infest lightly burned trees for several years after a fire. Until this discovery, salvage harvesting of all merchantable timber took place soon after a fire.

Another SFMN study found that it may be possible to "fire-proof" certain forests by manipulating the spatial arrangement of different forest types, especially white spruce and aspen. Many forest companies operating in western Canada rely on one of these two species. These findings may be translated into harvesting and silviculture strategies that exploit the properties of aspen stands to sustain the white spruce harvest.

The SFMN is also studying the impacts of climate change on future forests. (See article on page 72.) Based on forest fire simulations up to the period 2040 to 2060, researchers are predicting a major

62

change in western Canadian forests resulting from climate change, followed later by changes to eastern Canadian forests.

HARVESTING NATURALLY

Harvesting trees from healthy forests must also be done with care. Researchers are studying the aftermath of forest fires to learn the best ways to harvest trees while maintaining the integrity of forest ecosystems. The goal is to simulate forest conditions as they would be after a fire, since a more natural approach will help to maintain healthy, diverse ecosystems.

Forest fires seldom destroy all the trees in the area burned. Many fire-damaged trees continue to stand, and the patterns of living and dead trees, provide openings for a new forest, as well as habitat for wildlife species that live in the cavities of dead trees or in logs. While both harvesting and wildfire remove trees from the landscape, they leave behind different soil composition and erosion, different organisms, carbon budgets and long-term forest productivity. All of these need to be evaluated so that harvesting practices can have a disturbance pattern similar to that of fire.

The Ecosystem Management by Emulating Natural Disturbance (EMEND) project is part of the SFMN. It is studying which harvesting practices best emulate the effects of wildfire on forest ecosystems. It considers both timber and non-timber values, and other economic and social factors. EMEND includes partners from forest industry, governments, universities and other research organizations.

EMEND is one of the largest single-site forest experiments in the world. It has a 100-year timeframe and is believed to be the only study ever undertaken to monitor disturbance effects over the life cycle of a forest. Its innovative technology includes field tours and a web site, and it attracts visiting researchers and policy makers from around the world.

Forest companies are already putting into practice lessons learned from EMEND. In addition to cutting trees in a physical pattern similar to that left behind by a typical forest fire, harvesters leave clumps of trees in place for wildlife habitat and seed regeneration. Organic material is also left, to allow nutrients to return to the soil.

SALVAGE HARVESTING

The area burned by fire varies considerably from year to year, but for the past 40 years, the average annual area burned has been 2.8 million hectares—almost five times the size of Prince Edward Island. In unusually destructive years more commercially viable timber is destroyed by fire than is harvested. This loss significantly reduces the amount of wood that can be sustainably harvested from Canada's forests.

63

CANADIAN INTERAGENCY FOREST FIRE CENTRE
COOPERATION IS SPELLED 'CIFFC'

The Canadian Interagency Forest Fire Centre (CIFFC) was opened on June 2, 1982, to provide operational forest fire management services to member agencies. CIFFC provides information and services to these agencies to improve forest fire management in Canada.

A MODERN FUNDING APPROACH

The federal government contributes one-third of the Centre's operating costs. The remaining two-thirds is funded by the provinces and territories according to the amount of forest land they possess.

ADVANCED RESOURCE SHARING

Resources in Canada—equipment, personnel and aircraft—are shared under the Canadian Interagency Mutual Aid Resources Sharing (MARS) Agreement.

Agreements with the United States allow for quick movement of resources through Customs and Immigration—mandatory during a severe fire season.

In addition to cooperating with the U.S., CIFFC negotiates requests for assistance from other countries when required, and maintains membership with international organizations such as the North American Forestry Commission.

THE FLEET

CIFFC's national air tanker fleet consists of 13 Canadair CL-215s which are operated by the provinces on behalf of the country as a whole. Over 50 CL-215/415 aircraft, along with numerous land-based air tankers, operate in Canada. The CL215/415 is the number one resource request and has contributed to the overall fire suppression capability in initial attack and ground support.

THE HOT, DRY SEASON

During the fire season, CIFFC operates 24 hours a day, 7 days a week. An integral part of its operation is the fire "situation report" which provides information and intelligence to all member agencies. CIFFC also identifies available resources, including aircraft, personnel, equipment and specialty items such as communication networks and infrared line scanners.

The Centre maintains daily contact with the National Interagency Fire Centre in Boise, Idaho, and exchanges resources as needed across the international boundary.

THE FUTURE

The Canadian Council of Forest Ministers originally directed CIFFC to promote and improve fire management on a national level. The Centre continues to meet this challenge through its agreements and the development of exchange standards through various Working Groups.

Internationally, CIFFC will continue to promote Canadian fire management technology in the global marketplace.

Thanks to technological advances, forest managers can now salvage commercially viable lumber and pulpwood from burnt forests. One benefit of salvage harvesting is to reduce dead and damaged trees that would provide fuel for future fires or encourage insect outbreaks. On the other hand, burned forests provide a habitat for wildlife, seeds for certain trees, a microclimate for understorey vegetation, and a fount of nutrients. The key to successful salvage operations, therefore, is respect for the integrity of the ecosystem.

Provinces have inaugurated programs to reduce the loss of commercial timber. In Quebec, a special management plan, in areas heavily damaged by fires, insects, wind or diseases, prioritizes salvaging activities, including financial incentives.

The B.C. government recently signed agreements to create new forestry opportunities for 11 First Nations to harvest more than 2 million cubic metres of burnt timber and more than 1 million cubic metres of timber infested by the mountain pine beetle. The B.C. government's Forestry Innovation Investment is also cooperating with the Chinese Academy of Forestry to study how wood affected by wildfire and mountain pine beetles can be used in China.

THE FOREST INDUSTRY, A VITAL PARTNER

Although the forest industry has a vested interest in keeping a readily available supply of timber, companies who rely on the forests for their livelihood are aware that, as good corporate citizens, they have an obligation to put something back into the system to benefit future generations. Like the farmer who derives satisfaction from sending the best produce to market, the forest community—from the CEO of a giant firm to the logger to the sawmill operator—take pride in knowing that Canada is world-renowned for the quality of its timber and wood products. Some also participate in teams that find innovative ways to promote sustainable forestry.

One such team is the Forest Engineering Research Institute of Canada (FERIC), a research and development organization funded by forest companies, the federal government, the provinces and the Northwest Territories. FERIC's Wildland Fire Operations Research Group found that the exhaust systems of all-terrain vehicles (ATVs) were hot enough to ignite debris clinging to the system, possibly sparking an open fire. In February 2004, FERIC called for ATV manufacturers to address the high-heat problem, and asked owners to regularly remove debris from their exhaust systems and to carry basic firefighting equipment in their vehicles.

The vital partnership between the forest industry and fire management agencies has resulted in agreement to curtail industrial operations in times of high fire risk. Industry also trains employees up to the standards of Level 2 firefighting crews, so that forest company personnel, who are often the first to arrive at a fire, can fight it until professional fire crews arrive.

FIRE PREVENTION

Forest fires are started in one of two ways—by nature (usually lightning) or by people. Human-caused fires most often start from careless smoking or recreational activities. Although these fires are more common, they are normally detected quickly and controlled at a smaller size than natural fires. Nevertheless, educating people on how to prevent forest fires is a challenge.

65

Symbols, such as Smokey Bear, are highly effective for fire prevention—especially for youth. Smokey Bear is one of the best-known symbols in North America. Few children or adults in Canada have not heard his forest fire prevention message. Government agencies, media and youth groups cooperate in spreading his message. The Canadian Forestry Association is careful to note that Smokey's campaign is intended to reduce only the number of fires caused by human carelessness, and recognizes the place of forest fire management.

In Alberta, the Sustainable Resource Development department offers two highly successful programs for young people to learn about the natural environment and the challenges inherent in managing it. The Junior Forest Warden and the Junior Forest Ranger both emphasize the importance and role of fire in forest management.

Ontario uses "restricted fire zones" when conditions are so dry that extra precautions are required. The zones do not mean that hunting, fishing or camping are prohibited; they simply mean that fires are not allowed due to dry conditions. As soon as the region becomes damper, the restrictions are lifted. Ministry of Natural Resources posts signs along the roadway, as well as in camping spots, lodges, gas stations and stores. The Ministry provides information handouts at border crossings to those entering the province for outdoor recreational purposes, and utilizes the media for public announcements.

FIRE AND COMMUNITIES

The FireSmart manual describes how to prevent forest fires and protect homes and communities in the urban-wildland interface. Produced by Partners in Protection —an association of multi-level government agencies, the forest industry and non-governmental organizations—this comprehensive handbook provides knowledge, tools and examples of how to increase public safety, decrease structure loss, and reduce expenditures for evacuations and fire suppression.

FireSmart is both a concept and a product. Through a web site, www.partnersinprotection.ab.ca, a CD-ROM, and the distribution of over 10 000 paper copies, individuals and communities across Canada and internationally have begun to follow FireSmart guidelines.

The manual and web site explain how to identify and mitigate fire risks. They provide tools to assist homeowners, landscape planners and forest managers to assess hazards and risks. City planners are offered suggestions on how to

66

deal with interface emergencies and avoid tragedies. Training programs are listed, and tips for communication with parties at risk are included. British Columbia distributes a condensed 12-page version, the "Home Owners FireSmart" manual.

FireSmart is expanding to include forest landscapes. Research and operational trials will identify how forest management practices (harvest scheduling, cutting, road layouts, regeneration and stand tending) can reduce the area burned by unwanted wildfires and mitigate the risk associated with prescribed fires.

LOOKING AHEAD

Forests and forest fires have existed harmoniously for centuries. Only in the past 20 years have Canadians begun to realize the importance of forest fires and the role they play in forest ecosystems. In those 20 years, we have also made great strides towards sustainable forest management.

Fuelled by sophisticated technology and progressive research, Canada's forest scientists and managers have learned a great deal about the interaction of forests, fires and other natural phenomena. And they are

increasingly learning how to use this knowledge in their management plans and on-the-ground practices.

Under a changing climate, forest fire activity is expected to increase in many parts of Canada, especially the continental interior, due to longer fire seasons, increased ignitions, and more severe fire danger conditions due primarily to drought. This makes Canada's efforts to further understand the role of fires in shaping and renewing its forests even more urgent.

However, Canada is at the forefront of forest fire research and sustainable forest management. This combination bodes well for continued success in unlocking the secrets

of forest ecosystems, and the role of fire in those systems. It is also cause for optimism that people can continue to live and work safely in and near Canada's forests.

67

SPECIAL Articles

Forest Fires: **Part of Nature's Life Cycle**

Many people believe that a forest ecosystem is static. However, an understanding of the way the ecosystem functions over a period of several centuries or even several decades shows that forests are dynamic systems evolving in response to the effects of disturbances such as fires and insect outbreaks.

Fires occur frequently in the Canadian boreal forest. A flight over the boreal forest would show a mosaic of stands of different types of trees. These range from deciduous trees, to mixed stands of both deciduous and coniferous trees, to stands that are totally coniferous. This forest mosaic has resulted from fires that have occurred at different times. Fires are actually a part of nature's cleansing process which reduces the number of pests and the occurrence of diseases. Fires reduce the litter of dead and decaying leaves, logs and needles that accumulate on the forest floor. Another effect of fires is to reduce or eliminate the canopy, resulting in increased sunlight that stimulates regeneration from seeds and roots.

Fires also reset the successional clock of forest ecosystems, the process by which one plant community is succeeded by another. The first trees to grow after a fire are shade-intolerant, or pioneer trees. The shade of their canopy, allows coniferous trees, which will eventually dominate the area, to regenerate. This is why the variation in fire occurrence and intensity is partly responsible for the variety of forest types visible from the air.

REGIONAL DIVERSITY

Although the Canadian boreal forest is highly susceptible to fire, differences in the fire cycle do occur. Because the west has a less abundant rainfall, the area burned annually in the west is greater than in the east. In zones that have short fire cycles (50 years or less), the forest mosaic is largely made up of stands of pioneer, or deciduous species. However, a zone with an intermediate fire cycle (150 years) will have a mixture of

both pioneer species and shade-tolerant, or coniferous species. The frequency of fires is not the only factor affecting the diversity of forest stands. Other contributing factors include climate, species availability, and the physical set-up of the region.

A DYNAMIC FOREST

The pioneer species that most quickly regenerate in a forest after a fire include aspen, white birch, jack pine and lodgepole pine. These species all require full sunlight to thrive, and they are well adapted to recurring fires.

Aspen and birch are able to quickly re-establish themselves through vegetative reproduction—simply by sprouting from the stumps and roots of burned trees. These two species are also able to re-colonize burned sites by producing an abundance of seeds that can be blown by the wind over long distances. Jack and lodgepole pines depend on fire to regenerate. Their seeds are in serotinous cones, which are protected by a waxy coating and which require the heat from a fire to release them. Fire also produces favourable conditions for their seeds to germinate: nutrients are released in the soil, mineral soil is exposed, competing species are eliminated and the amount of sunlight that reaches the forest floor is increased.

Other species, such as the black spruce, have semi-serotinous cones. Black spruce may also become established in the years following a fire, but they grow slower in full sunlight than jack pine and aspen do. However, if fire does not recur for more than 100 years, the early pioneer trees die and are replaced by black

69

spruce saplings that have been growing in the under-storey. Black spruce can persist in stands because of its ability to sprout from roots, stems or branches—even in shady conditions.

Other shade-tolerant species can become established under the shady cover. Species such as the balsam fir, white spruce or white cedar have no special adaptations to fire; therefore, they must colonize a burned area from an unburned area. These species require long periods to stage a comeback after fire. Thus, aspen and birch are gradually replaced by balsam fir and, in some regions, by white cedar from deciduous stands that have not been burned in more than 150 years. Because extensive fires place balsam fir and cedar at a disadvantage, these species are quite rare in areas that are repeatedly severely burned or where fires are large.

FIRE AND WILDLIFE

Nearly all animals inhabiting Canada's forests have adapted well to the regular return of wildland fire. The evidence shows that fires do not completely destroy wildlife populations since most animals are able to avoid fires by burrowing, running or flying away, or escaping into water. The usual victims of forest fires are nestlings or the very young. Although this is regrettable, it is a fact of nature. Fire can also be detrimental to endangered species; an example is the woodland caribou which like to feed on old-growth tree lichen.

A positive after-effect of fire is that nutrients are more abundant and accessible to vegetation, at least for a certain time; this produces conditions favourable for plant growth. In addition, within a few days, burned timber attracts beetles that in turn attract birds.

When fire kills trees, the threat from insects or diseases in the forest is reduced. Fire reduces the forest canopy, and the increased sunlight on the forest floor stimulates regeneration from seeds and roots. In the first year after the fire, trees are rapidly re-established on the

For example, the black-backed woodpecker is very abundant in recently burned stands, but quite rare in older stands. Insects also attract omnivorous animals, such as the bear, fox, badger, skunk and other species. This is the way that biodiversity is re-established in a burned-over area. New growth in the recently burned forest also attracts grazers, such as deer and moose, which feed on the tender shoots of vegetation.

WHAT HAVE WE LEARNED?

A sustainable forest management approach advocates preserving ecosystem diversity to conserve the habitat of the majority of living organisms. Knowledge of natural dynamics associated with forest fires and other disturbances is essential to implementing such an approach. Even though Canada has excellent systems for protecting forests from fire, it is impossible to completely eliminate forest fires from many ecosystems. Understanding forest fires will allow us to use their positive effects for forest management.

site—this is evident by the vigorous growth of the aspen root suckers. In addition, the remaining burned timber attracts a number of beetles, which serve as food for birds. Within 50 years of a forest fire, the forest is mainly composed of deciduous trees and their canopy provides shade for the understory. One hundred years after the fire, the dominant trees are still deciduous, but coniferous trees are growing in the understory. At 150 years after the fire, the forest is dominated by coniferous species that were able to establish themselves in the shade.

This photo sequence shows:
1) A fire
2) The regrowth of aspen, 1 year after fire
3) Burned tree with black-backed woodpecker, 1 year after fire
4) A 50-year stand
5) A 100-year stand
6) 150 years of growth
7) Old-growth forest (with gap dynamics)

71

Things Are Heating Up with Climate Change

Fire has been an important factor in the Canadian forest ecosystem since the last Ice Age. This is particularly true in Canada's vast boreal forest region, where fire is critical to the very existence of primary boreal species such as pine, spruce and aspen and in shaping landscape diversity.

INTERACTIONS BETWEEN CLIMATE, WEATHER AND FIRE

Climate—the long-term average of weather conditions—and associated day-to-day weather are dynamic and constantly changing. Climate and weather conditions are influenced by natural and human forces such as changes in the earth's orbit, changes in solar output, and changes in atmospheric gas composition, primarily as a result of greenhouse gases released by human activities. In Canada, weather is the most important natural factor that influences forest fires. Day-to-day weather causes lightning ignitions, determines the moisture content of trees and of woody debris on the forest floor (that serve as fuel) and can fan fires that are already burning. Hot, dry and windy conditions, continued over lengthy periods, are very conducive to fire activity.

While weather and climate affect fire activity, fire may also influence climate. Climate change may cause more fire, which then releases more carbon from the forest; this increase in atmospheric greenhouse gas concentrations may contribute to further climate change. In addition, evidence indicates that smoke reduces precipitation and increases the likelihood that lightning will ignite fires. This mutual feedback appears to be a global phenomenon. In Siberia, for example, more than 10 million hectares have burned annually in recent years. However, natural factors will limit a potentially runaway scenario. More fire will also change the vegetation. For example, in some parts of Canada's forests, early successional deciduous trees will help to slow fire movement because they do not burn as quickly as later successional coniferous trees.

EFFECTS ON CARBON DYNAMICS

Climate change will also influence carbon dynamics (the fluctuation and distribution of carbon in different parts of the ecosystem) of the forest through changes in fire activity. In addition to fire, other natural disturbances—such as insects and disease—may cause Canada's forests to release rather than trap carbon. Over the last two decades, forest fires have burned an average of two to three million hectares annually in Canada—the equivalent of half the size of Nova Scotia burning every year. The method through which fires release carbon is through direct combustion emissions. Direct combustion occurs when the biomass (living or dead organic matter in the ecosystem) is engulfed in flames during a fire or through smouldering.

Over the last 40 years, this has accounted for almost 20 percent of the amount of carbon released through fossil fuel emissions in Canada. In addition to the direct combustion losses of carbon, vegetation killed by fire decomposes, causing additional loss of carbon from the forest. The amount of carbon that the forest normally takes up is also reduced during the first few years following fire because the new, young vegetation stores less carbon than a more mature forest. The forest carbon dynamics following fire are less well known than the combustion losses, but are likely of similar importance.

72

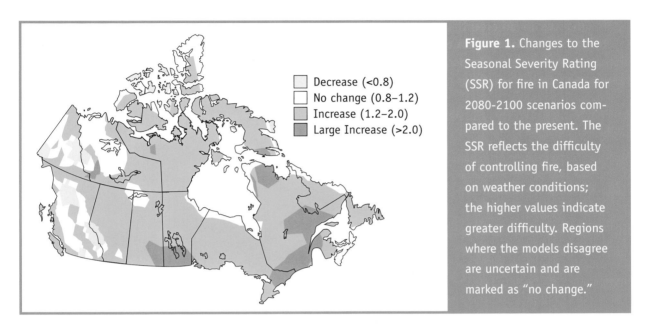

Figure 1. Changes to the Seasonal Severity Rating (SSR) for fire in Canada for 2080-2100 scenarios compared to the present. The SSR reflects the difficulty of controlling fire, based on weather conditions; the higher values indicate greater difficulty. Regions where the models disagree are uncertain and are marked as "no change."

Legend:
- Decrease (<0.8)
- No change (0.8–1.2)
- Increase (1.2–2.0)
- Large Increase (>2.0)

LOOKING INTO THE 21ST CENTURY

How will climate change influence forest fires in the 21st century? Estimates from global circulation models and regional climate models suggest that much of Canada will experience more fire in the 21st century. In general, there will be more periods of weather conducive to forest fires—hot, dry and windy. Based on the present situation and our climate projections, the best estimates to date are that by the end of the 21st century, the area burned annually could double. This change will not likely be evenly distributed across the country; some areas may experience less fire, at least temporarily, because of increases in precipitation.

Some projections of the Seasonal Severity Rating (SSR) for Canada are shown in Figure 1. Since SSR often correlates well with the area burned, this map illustrates what could happen in the future. Increases in severity and difficulty in controlling fire are expected throughout much of the boreal forest, the area of Canada currently experiencing the most fire. Recent research also suggests a possible lengthening of the fire season in most areas, increases in fire severity and intensity, and increases in both people-caused and lightning ignitions throughout the 21st century. Canadians who live and work in the forest will, therefore, be at a greater risk from forest fires, as will communities and infrastructure in forested regions.

Future research is aimed at refining these climate change estimates of fire activity using dynamic models of fire and landscape vegetation. Also helpful will be models of the role of fire management and fire suppression activities.

73

Disturbances **and** Renewal **in the Forest**

Disturbances are an essential part of forest renewal. Typically, these disturbances are large, uncontrolled fires or insect outbreaks. Both types of disturbances play major roles in determining the biological, structural and landscape diversity of Canada's forests. However, the intensity and impacts of these two perturbations differ considerably.

DIFFERENCES BETWEEN FIRE AND INSECT OUTBREAKS

Most forest fires cause little damage, but 3 percent of the fires that occur cause about 97 percent of the damage. Fires can damage all the trees in a stand, usually within days or weeks.

By contrast, insect outbreaks are generally extensive. Their occurrence is more cyclical than fires, and they attack large areas at the same time. In addition, insects often attack only specific host trees and the damage is developed over a period of years. Even host trees that are not killed usually experience reduced growth. Yet it is often difficult to find the insects that caused the damage between outbreaks.

These differences between fires and insect outbreaks explain, in part, their different impacts on forest structure and diversity. As an example of their intensity and impacts, the 2003 fires in British Columbia burned an estimated 265 373 hectares; by contrast, in the last four years the mountain pine beetle killed trees over a cumulative area of 4.2 million hectares.

CHANGES IN THE FOREST

Forest ecosystems experience repeated successional cycles of establishment, development and renewal. During each cycle, the sequence moves from short-lived herbs and grasses to shrubs, to fast-growing, shade-intolerant trees, and eventually—as a closed forest canopy is established—to slow-growing, shade-tolerant trees. Insect outbreaks and fires interrupt

this sequence naturally by shifting the forest towards younger age plants and the earlier successional stages. In contrast to extensive fires, some insect outbreaks open gaps in the forest canopy, permitting the development of multi-aged stands that are typical of old-growth forests. Both of these disturbances change the physical structure of stands by removing weakened and less competitive trees. While dead trees may become fuel, they may also serve as habitat for a variety of plant species, vertebrates, fungi and insects that are essential for the proper functioning of forests.

Most insects are beneficial. However, several dozen are considered to be pests because they interfere, or compete, with forest growth and productivity. Fire, too, has long been considered a competitor of the forest industry. Substantial effort—in terms of money, research and human resources—has been expended to suppress both fire and pest populations in situations where productive forests and other values were at risk. Unfortunately, these suppression activities have produced some unforeseen consequences. In some areas, fire control has allowed succession to proceed without interruption until much of the landscape is covered with a preponderance of mature forest stands. These stands may be particularly vulnerable to major outbreaks of forest insects. Fire control sometimes also interferes with other beneficial processes: fires regulate some insect and disease outbreaks, and they limit susceptible groups of forest plants. Thus fires contribute to the overall health and productivity of many forested ecosystems.

An ecosystem feature of fire- and insect-killed vegetation is that nutrients recycle faster than they do in undisturbed forests. This process releases accumulations of biomass, energy and nutrients into the system. The resources produced are exploited by plant species that invade the site and launch another successional sequence. In addition, standing dead timber attracts beetles and other insects that initiate the breakdown of debris to release nutrients that can encourage new growth. These insects also attract the birds and mammals that feed on them, helping to re-colonize disturbed areas that would have been abandoned by wildlife before or during the disturbance.

INCREASING UNDERSTANDING IS KEY

Several tools are available to protect people, property, and productive forests from uncontrolled and catastrophic forest disturbances. Pests can be controlled through the increased use of environmentally friendly procedures, such as partial cutting. Prescribed burning may help to reduce the risk of fires

and future insect outbreaks. An understanding of fire and pest behaviour is essential to help manage Canada's forest systems. We need to know how outbreaks start and spread, their immediate impacts, and the long-term socio-economic and environmental consequences of either controlling them or allowing them to run their course.

Climate change presents a particular challenge to this understanding. The effects of climate change on the damage patterns caused by fire and insect populations are not yet understood. This knowledge gap will directly affect depletion forecasts, hazard rating procedures and long-term planning for harvest queues, ecological values and control requirements. For example, because the potential for fire often increases in stands after insect attack, uncertainties in future insect damage patterns magnify uncertainties in future fire frequencies, intensities and extent.

Many Canadians value wild, pristine and unmanaged landscapes. At the same time, however, the country derives considerable wealth from forests. Currently, the combined annual depletion from pests and fires of Canadian forests' productive capacity is larger than annual harvests of forest products. This dilemma could accelerate our search for a more complete understanding of how disturbances affect our forests. Canada must seek a balance between encouraging productive forests, maintaining wilderness areas, and supporting thriving communities near forests.

Top left: forest tent caterpillar

Top right: spruce budworm

Right: mountain pine beetle

75

For the RECORD

Canadians have a high regard for forests, and we have a natural interest in keeping them healthy and abundant. In recent years, Canadian newspaper articles and television and radio broadcasts have focused on controversial issues related to our forests and forest management practices. Important facts have been presented and spirited public discussions have ensued. But media coverage has not always looked into these issues in depth, and discussions have not always been based on knowledge necessary for complete understanding. Consequently, media attention and public response may inadvertently have spawned various myths and misperceptions.

This section of the report aims to clear up some of these misunderstandings. Canadians need to know that the organizations responsible for forest management policies and practices are dealing with our finest resources in a careful and responsible manner. To explain current knowledge and handling of two complex, often misunderstood and sometimes controversial issues, this section records explanations from specialists in the field.

Genetically modified plants constitute one area where misunderstandings may have arisen due to incomplete understanding of the complex issues involved. Dr. Ariane Plourde is Research Director of Forest Biology at the Canadian Forest Service's Laurentian Forestry Centre. We asked her about genetically modified trees:

"Do genetically modified trees pose a threat to our forests and the environment?"

Dr. Plourde's response follows:

While one can appreciate people's concern over the use of genetically modified trees, there is insufficient evidence at this time to suggest that genetically modified trees pose a threat to Canada's forests or the environment. Genetic engineering research on trees is in the early stages and there are no commercial genetically modified forest plantations in Canada.

In fact, the Canadian Forest Service is doing targeted research on the potential effects of genetically modified trees to ensure that the public's concerns are addressed. Research scientists are examining the impacts of genetically modified trees on the diversity of populations of the same and other species, as well as the direct or indirect impacts on other organisms.

These effects are being studied through four self-contained and highly controlled genetically modified trees field trials in Quebec. All four field trials are subjected to careful scrutiny of disposal of material and land use following field tests, and are monitored for long-term containment of genetic material. Research is also being conducted on persistence and degradation of the introduced DNA segments over time. This research will provide support for the development of scientifically sound regulatory guidelines in Canada.

76

To protect the surrounding area, the trial site is clearly delineated and guard rows of non-modified trees have been established. Moreover, the site is separated by a buffer zone of at least 10 metres from other trees of related species. Flowering is rigorously monitored and precautions are taken each year to prevent pollen and seeds from being released into the environment. This field study will help answer many environmental questions.

Five targeted research areas of applied biotechnology are being studied by the Canadian Forest Service. These include identifying genetically superior trees and genetic diversity; regenerating trees through tissue culture, including somatic embryogenesis (a form of tree propagation); improving trees through genetic engineering; protecting forests using biological control methods, including genetically engineered insect viruses; and assessing environmental impacts of biotechnology-derived products.

CFS researchers are conducting studies on gene traits of particular interest: control of resistance to insects and disease, resistance to abiotic stresses like drought, and lignin content. (Lignin, a component of tree cells that gives rigidity to the plant, is closely associated with cellulose and must be dissolved in the process of paper production.) Other genes of public interest are the regulatory genes, such as those involved in the expression of traits in different parts of the trees over time. A new science called functional genomics will help to explain why certain trees exhibit particular traits and others do not, and will assist in selecting superior genotypes. In the future, it may be possible to switch on insect- or disease-resistant genes that are naturally silent in certain tree species. Genetically modified trees may also form an integral part of Canada's solution to the potentially devastating effects of foreign invasive insects and diseases. ■

77

Clearcutting is another area of forest management that is often misunderstood. In the past several decades we have seen images in the media of once lush forested areas that have been laid waste, and many Canadians have become concerned about how Canada's natural forests are being harvested. To provide clarity with regard to clearcutting, we asked Hans Ottens, Coordinator of Forestry Practices in the Science Programs of CFS:

"Is clearcutting an acceptable forestry practice?"

This was his response to our question:

It is difficult to provide a clearly positive answer, because this question often evokes images of barren wastelands, based on media coverage. There is no denying it—areas that have been clearcut are unattractive. And many of the concerns Canadians have voiced over the years relate to very large clearcuts which have sometimes resulted in soil erosion, landslides or inadequate natural reforestation. However, these situations are exceptions.

Today natural resource managers pay a great deal of attention to the aesthetic and environmental impacts of clearcutting. Through advanced clearcutting practices and techniques, they attempt to emulate natural disturbances such as wildfire and blowdown. This kind of modified clearcutting has become an integral part of Canada's sustainable forest management. For example, the Ontario government's guideline, *The Forest Management Guide for Natural Disturbance Pattern Emulation*, advises forest managers on how to size and arrange harvest areas and regeneration activities to simulate the way in which natural fire disturbs the forest.

Selecting an appropriate harvesting practice is important. The forest manager must balance the sustainability of social, economic and environmental elements. Decreasing availability of commercial wood, increasing demands for recreational and non-timber values, dramatic increase in scientific knowledge and ecological awareness, and livelihood of rural communities often result in competing interests.

From a forest management perspective, clearcutting is one of two main silvicultural systems aimed at maintaining even-aged forests. The other is the Shelterwood System, used for species of intermediate shade tolerance like white pine and red oak. Under even-aged systems, an entire forest (or a component thereof) is harvested in a single operation. A third, the Selection Silvicultural System, used in Canada and around the world, is employed to maintain uneven-aged forests.

Of the three systems, clearcutting remains the dominant forest operation for about 85 percent of the million or so hectares harvested in Canada annually. However, regeneration treatments are part of this system: artificial regeneration, such as tree planting and seeding, and natural regeneration, where seed and cones in logging debris, seed trees and standing timber are left to flourish naturally.

78

In boreal conifer forests, clearcutting is usually the most appropriate harvesting technique. Here clearcutting comes closest to mimicking natural disturbances. In the more southerly mixed-wood and hardwood forests, some form of selection or partial harvesting may be preferred, because it comes closer to natural disturbance effects common in these sorts of forests. The forests we now have are the result of human and natural influences, and proper management of forests with even-aged stands can prevent catastrophic fire or insect outbreaks.

So is clearcutting an acceptable forestry practice? It all depends on the type of forest you are working with. Clearcutting is one method used by professional foresters to harvest, salvage and renew most types of Canadian forest. Where uneven-aged management is appropriate, increasingly selection silviculture is practised. But Canada continues to refine its harvesting and tending practices, guided by the principles of sustainable development, so that all systems will have positive effects for all forest stakeholders. ■

79

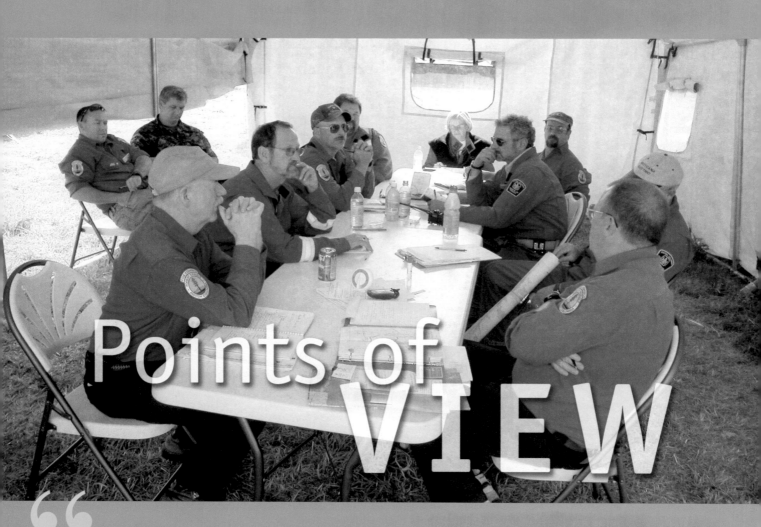

Points of VIEW

"What **LESSONS** did you learn from dealing with the fire situation in Kelowna this summer?

What **IMPROVEMENTS** would you make to address future fires?

Did the situation create any new **OPPORTUNITIES** for you or the community?"

It started with lightning. Early on August 16, 2003, a bolt ignited in Okanagan Mountain Provincial Park, south of Kelowna. As the fire spread, it became a rank six firestorm, the highest possible level. In just four days, the fire had destroyed the park, jumped a 50-metre-wide fireguard and was approaching Kelowna. Nearly 30 000 Kelowna residents were eventually evacuated. In one night alone, 223 houses were lost.

The Kelowna blaze, which consumed homes and property well into September, was the most destructive wildfire in B.C.'s recent history. Can we salvage anything from such destruction? To find out, we asked fire experts, emergency response staff, firefighters and residents to share their views on lessons learned, recommendations and opportunities arising from the firestorm.

FIRE EXPERTS

Peter Fuglem
Director, Protection Branch, B.C. Ministry of Forests.
Tim Lynham
Forest Fire Research Officer, Canadian Forest Service—came from Ontario to relieve fire analysts at the Kamloops Regional Fire Centre.
Judi Beck
Fire Behaviour Specialist, B.C. Ministry of Forests—monitored the Kelowna fire.

With hundreds of wildfires burning throughout British Columbia last summer, many of them serious and near populated areas, the province's firefighting resources were stretched to the limit. The situation was eye-opening for Peter Fuglem. "The provincial forest service had always viewed years like 1985 as the worst-case scenario. But in 2003, we found that things could be much worse. The drought was more severe and widespread, and the effort we had to expend on forest fires was more than twice that of 1985." This has changed how the ministry views the future. "Before this summer, we thought we had a sufficient plan for contingency resources. But we know now that we have to be ready for something much bigger and worse."

In spite of the challenging conditions, says Mr. Fuglem, the province, with help from across the country, responded extremely well. "The assistance from others went above and beyond our expectations. It's a valuable lesson for anyone in such a situation in the future—Canada is the kind of country where we can count on each other to help out."

Much assistance was sent B.C.'s way by the Canadian Interagency Forest Fire Centre (CIFFC) (see text box on page 64). Based in Winnipeg and funded by the provinces, territories and federal government,

Tim Lynham at the Great Lakes Forestry Centre, Sault Ste. Marie, Ontario

the CIFFC monitors wildfires across Canada and shifts firefighting resources accordingly. Says Tim Lynham, "The summer of 2003 was a big test for this resource-sharing arrangement. Not only was the situation in B.C. critical, but there were major fires in other parts of the country at the same time. With this arrangement, resources were shifted where they were needed and were used effectively." In fact, the CIFFC arranged for Mr. Lynham to help out in B.C.

But is the CIFFC enough? "The province must have a larger pool of contingency resources available for managing forest fires," says Peter Fuglem. "We were lucky this year that firefighting resources in other provinces, except for Alberta, were not terribly busy when our fires struck. But what happens if different regions are hit at the same time?" B.C. must look at alternatives, he says, including firefighting resources available from industry.

Contingency planning is even more important because of current climatic patterns, according to Mr. Lynham. "Canada should be prepared for further serious wildfire outbreaks in the future. If climate change continues to bring warmer, drier weather, there is a greater probability that a lightning strike or a dropped cigarette will actually start a fire."

The Kelowna fire's scope meant the community had an insatiable appetite for information, according to Dr. Judi Beck, who kept fire prediction information flowing throughout the incident. "Having a B.C. forest service liaison officer in the emergency centre made my job easier," she says. Unlike with past fires, when she had to attend media briefings herself, the liaison officer handled this function, translating her technical information into lay terms and making sure the media and emergency centre staff were up to date. This left Dr. Beck free to concentrate on fire forecasting.

All three fire experts see an upside to the province's experience this summer. Says Tim Lynham, "The B.C. fires should open the door to more study and discussion of using prescribed fires to clear out deadwood and other fuel and to regenerate forests, especially in interface areas" (where forests meet populated areas).

Peter Fuglem agrees that B.C. must look seriously at fuel management. Historically, he explains, Okanagan forests were subject to frequent low-intensity fires. But now, with the area a popular viewscape,

Judi Beck discussing fire behaviour forecasts with the Fire Prevention and Risk Management team outside the Kelowna Fire Hall

fire suppression has caused fuel to build up. "We've done fuel management around many communities to one level or another," he says, "but we need to keep moving ahead. Everyone with a land management role, including landowners, has a responsibility here."

Dr. Beck and Mr. Lynham agree that landowners play a key role in fire safety. Both would like to see building codes, community plans and even insurance companies take more account of wildfire mitigation. According to Dr. Beck, forensic investigation since the fire has unearthed a number of measures that could make environments more fire-resistant, including limiting cedar shake roofs and designing breaks in cedar fencing and plantings, which can serve as connective wicks for fire.

"People have to do things, as individuals and as communities, to make their areas more fire-safe," says Peter Fuglem. "They have to be prepared. The fires in B.C. this summer, reinforced by the intense fires in California, should change people's thinking."

83

EMERGENCY RESPONSE

Sid LeBeau
Assistant Chief, Kelowna Fire Department—administers
the Kelowna/Central Okanagan regional emergency plan.
Ron Mattiussi
City of Kelowna—was Manager of the Emergency Opera-
tions Centre.
Karen Cairns
City of Kelowna—was Public Information Director at the
Emergency Operations Centre.

Ron Mattiussi at a press conference

Once the fire broke out, officials in Kelowna and the Central Okanagan Regional District set up the Emergency Operations Centre (EOC). About three dozen people staffed the centre, with others contributing as needed.

All three emergency response officials stressed that it was immensely valuable to have a regional emergency plan in place already. The plan worked well because regular practice and drills are an essential part of it—a part that really paid off, say those on the scene. "Everyone in the EOC worked together; everyone was focused," says Sid LeBeau. "There were people working there who had been evacuated from their homes, one who had lost a home. It didn't matter."

Mr. LeBeau says that because the region's emergency plan is compatible with the B.C. Emergency Response Management System, it was easy to communicate with provincial agencies, a big advantage in such a crisis. But he adds that, while municipalities in B.C. are required to adopt an emergency plan, regional districts aren't. He would recommend that all regional districts have a plan which is compatible with the province's.

Early on, emergency staff made a discovery: the digital map systems for Central Okanagan Regional District didn't mesh with those for Kelowna. Two teams of experts had to quickly integrate the two systems to help with evacuations, should they become necessary. "Emergencies don't respect boundaries," says Ron Mattiussi. "Quality, up-to-date mapping is crucial for so many things—good on-the-ground reconnaissance, orderly evacuation, recovery from the emergency. Getting people out fast depends on good mapping." Karen Cairns adds, "Municipalities and the regional districts or counties next to them have to make sure their mapping systems are compatible before an emergency like this arises."

Emergency staff also learned that such a large-scale disaster requires a constant supply of people. "We were in emergency mode for about three weeks," says Mr. Mattiussi. "That's a very long time to be in a state of constant readiness." Sid LeBeau adds, "It's important to line up alternates."

One of the EOC's main roles was updating the public about the fire. According to Karen Cairns, cooperation with the media was key to keeping the community informed and calm. The media coverage was aided tremendously, she says, by the willingness of key officials like the EOC manager and the fire chief to be available for media interviews. "At a time like this, the public wants, and deserves, to hear from the people in charge," Ms. Cairns says. She suggests that key emergency officials get training if they are uncomfortable speaking to the media.

Coordination between municipal and provincial jurisdictions was a vital area, according to the interviewees. Ron Mattiussi said that while the municipal and provincial firefighters both performed well, the 350 fires raging simultaneously stretched provincial resources and made on-the-ground coordination difficult.

Did this devastating fire create any opportunities? Yes, says Sid LeBeau. "For the Kelowna Fire Department, there's an opportunity to go around to other communities that haven't dealt with such an experience and train them on handling forest fires of this magnitude."

Ron Mattiussi thinks communities can learn more about fire mitigation and homeowners can be more proactive themselves. People who live in forested areas should take steps to lessen fire risks. Trees should be well spaced and pine cones, branches and needles should be regularly removed.

FIREFIGHTERS

Brian Kempf
B.C. Ministry of Forests, Incident Commander, Provincial Fire Management Team—oversaw provincial forest firefighters in the area.
Gerry Zimmermann
Chief, Kelowna Fire Department.
Shawn O'Reilly
Station Officer, Kelowna Fire Department.

Fire Chief Gerry Zimmerman

As the Kelowna firestorm grew, hundreds of firefighters—municipal and provincial alike—came from across the province and the country to combat the blaze.

For Brian Kempf, the biggest lesson was the importance of teamwork: "With the number of agencies and people involved in Kelowna, I learned firsthand how necessary it is." The emergency team, which exceeded 1300 at one point, was one of the largest Mr. Kempf ever worked with, and he praised their efforts. The team

Brian Kempf (far left) taking a well-earned break with his colleagues

worked under the Incident Command System (ICS), which B.C. adopted a number of years ago. Says Mr. Kempf, "Because the personnel involved were all familiar with the ICS, they used common terminology and understood the command structure, which made it easier for people from different jurisdictions to work together."

Gerry Zimmermann agrees that the firefighters worked well together, but he is less positive about the coordination between government agencies. "It was unclear to the Kelowna firefighters just which of the three agencies present was actually in charge—the B.C. Fire Commissioner's office; the B.C. Forest Service, which was in charge of the forested areas; or Provincial Emergency Preparedness." Mr. Zimmermann sees value in a provincial agency taking charge in a large fire, but says it's crucial to decide which one beforehand so that command structures are clear.

For Brian Kempf, the sheer size and intensity of the fire was a learning experience. Shawn O'Reilly, who led municipal crews on the ground, agrees. "At one point, we were pumping thousands of gallons of water onto that fire and it had no impact. In the 28 years I've been a career firefighter, I've never seen anything like it."

Mr. O'Reilly still wonders what might have happened had Kelowna firefighters been able to help sooner. For the first couple of days, while the fire was in the forest and thus under provincial jurisdiction, the municipal crews were not allowed to fight the blaze.

Brian Kempf agrees in theory that forestry and structural firefighters could collaborate sooner, but he's not sure the amount of training required would be worth it. "We have different training, different equipment, different firefighting techniques," he says. Mr. O'Reilly thinks the firestorm allowed firefighters to bridge those differences. "Really, we learned from each other," he

Shawn O'Reilly being interviewed by the press

says. "Our structural firefighters had a chance to learn how to go after a forest fire. And the forestry firefighters had a chance to learn what our equipment can do."

Mr. O'Reilly and Mr. Kempf also discovered how much the community appreciated their efforts to save land and homes. Both describe the outpouring of support from citizens who brought firefighters food and water and lined the roads with thank-you signs. Gerry Zimmermann also emphasizes the community spirit during the fire. He thinks it helped that residents got all the news, including whether they had lost their homes, as quickly as possible. "I can't stress enough the importance of getting the community behind you in an emergency like this one," he says. "Without that, you're fighting more fronts than just the fire itself."

For Mr. Kempf, one positive outcome is that residents are thinking more about fuel management and fire safety. "Around B.C., people have talked about fuel management for a long time, but most haven't actually bought into the program. People worry about prescribed fire getting out of control and they don't want the smoke around their communities. But now, people may think differently."

Denis Hostland

RESIDENTS

Denis Hostland
lost his 3300-square-foot home in the firestorm.
Murray Roed's
house was one of dozens to burn in the Crawford Estates subdivision.
Kevin and Alisa Brownlee
lost their 18-month-old dream home in Kettle Valley.

Denis Hostland's biggest lesson concerns forest management in B.C. Okanagan Mountain Provincial Park, where the fire started, is a Class A park with no forest management. In recent years, says Mr. Hostland, especially after the mountain pine beetle infestation, the province was warned by forest companies and its own staff to clear out the deadwood and other fuel. "People were telling the province that the park was a tinderbox, that if a match was dropped, that would be it. The province had ample opportunity to do something about the situation, but it didn't."

Mr. Hostland adds, "The province has been pandering to environmental groups that say the park should remain in its natural state. But ironically, the province's decision to hide behind the Class A designation and preserve the park in its natural state, instead of intervening and managing it, has caused the park's destruction."

Murray Roed agrees. "To all tree lovers out there, I can only say look at what happened to us. If our forest companies could have operated freely, and if the provincial government had allowed forest

87

The Brownlees and their new home, under construction

management in Okanagan Mountain Park, as was recommended many times, life here would be different." Mr. Roed also questions Kelowna: "There has been no urban forest management that I know of in the city, except that done by power and telephone companies along their right-of-ways. I hope that now this issue will be addressed."

What was the biggest lesson for Kevin and Alisa Brownlee? "Review your insurance," says Kevin. "When we had to cost everything for replacement, we realized we were way underinsured." The same realization hit the Hostlands and the Roeds, whose contents weren't adequately covered.

The Brownlees, whose house burned despite being built to the most recent fire standards, also say they didn't take the fire seriously enough at first. Murray Roed and Denis Hostland say the same. "Next time I wouldn't be so naive," says Mr. Hostland. "My wife and I left for Vancouver before our area was under evacuation, and my wife packed some photos just in case. I remember laughing, saying 'We have the second largest population in the area outside Vancouver. They're not going to let us burn.' We lost everything, except for those photos she'd packed. I thought it couldn't happen to us. The truth is, it can happen to anybody."

It can even happen to people whose homes are not surrounded by trees, say the Brownlees. "It's important for people to know that we don't live in the forest," says Kevin. "We live half a kilometre away, in a developed community where there are only a few small trees planted along the sidewalks." Alisa's parents also lost their home, which was well away from the treeline.

The Brownlees and Denis Hostland commend Kelowna firefighters for trying to save homes from a fire that was out of control. Says Mr. Hostland, "They did a spectacular job under horrendous circumstances. The city couldn't get involved until the fire hit the Kelowna boundaries, and by then it was a wild animal."

88

Murray Roed disagrees. "The city fire department lacked an effective contingency plan to protect highly vulnerable localities like Crawford Estates, which was clearly in the line of fire for at least a week before its partial destruction. In my opinion, fire management lacked vision." Mr. Roed, a geological consultant in the process of mapping Okanagan Mountain Park until the fire destroyed his files and photos, tells Canadians, "If you live in a forest fringe zone, press city, regional and other governments to develop management and emergency plans."

All four residents were quick to praise the hundreds of emergency volunteers and local residents who helped them through their loss. Mr. Roed singles out the evacuation crews for working efficiently without loss of life. Mr. Hostland says the caring volunteers in the fire's aftermath made a huge difference to his ability to cope. "People sure came together," says Alisa Brownlee. "It taught us that 'love thy neighbour' really means something."

CONCLUSION

From coast to coast, Canadians watched with horror and sympathy as Kelowna was assaulted by fire. But we can take away from this disaster far more than images of devastation. The need to adopt and practise emergency plans, to share and coordinate resources from different jurisdictions, to handle public information properly, to improve fuel management and fire safety, to review fire insurance and take fire threats seriously—these are valuable lessons for all Canadians, especially those near forested areas.

A water bomber taking off from a lake with its precious cargo

We can also learn from the human side of this disaster. Thanks to the volunteers who flocked to help, the citizens who opened their homes, the individuals who gave their all to fight the fire and manage the emergency, no matter how quickly the Kelowna fire destroyed property, something meaningful was rebuilt in its wake.

GLOSSARY

ABIOTIC STRESS	Stress induced by the non-living component of the environment.
BLOWDOWN	Tree or trees felled or broken off by wind.
BOREAL FOREST	One of the three main forest zones in the world located in northern regions and is characterized by the predominance of conifers.
CLIMATE CHANGE	An alteration in measured quantities (e.g., precipitation, temperature, radiation, wind and cloudiness) within the climate system that departs significantly from previous average conditions and is seen to endure, bringing about corresponding changes in ecosystems and socioeconomic activity.
COMMERCIAL FOREST	Forest land that is able to grow commercial timber within an acceptable time frame and is designated for such a purpose.
CROWN FIRE	A fire that advances through the crown fuel layer, the upper part of the tree bearing live branches and foliage.
DUFF LAYER	A general term referring to the litter and humus layers of the forest floor.
ECOSYSTEM	A dynamic system of plants, animals and other organisms, together with the non-living components of the environment, functioning as an interdependent unit.
EVEN-AGED	Of a forest stand or forest type in which relatively small age differences exist between individual trees (usually 10 to 20 years).
FUNCTIONAL GENOMICS	Predicting biological function of genes and proteins from their primary sequence.
GAP DYNAMICS	The change in space and time in the pattern, frequency, size, and successional processes of forest canopy gaps caused by the fall or death of one or more canopy trees.
GENOTYPE	An individual hereditary constitution derived from its parents and forming a unique combination of genes; sometimes referring to trees having similar genetic constitutions with regard to certain common, identifiable, genetic characteristics, expressed in distinctive features.
GREENHOUSE GASES	Those gases, such as water vapour, carbon dioxide, tropospheric ozone, nitrous oxide and methane, that are transparent to solar radiation but opaque to longwave radiation. Their action is similar to that of glass in a greenhouse.
HARDWOOD (DECIDUOUS TREE)	Tree whose leaves are not persistent and fall off at the end of a defined growing season or during a period of temperature or moisture stress.
HOLISTIC APPROACH	Broad brush approach based on a theory according to which a whole cannot be analyzed without considering the sum of its parts or reduced to discrete elements.
LADDER FUELS	Fuels that provide vertical continuity between the surface fuels and crown fuels in a forest stand, thus contributing to the ease of torching and crowning, e.g., tall shrubs, small-sized trees, bark flakes, tree lichens.

90

MOP-UP (FIRE)	The act of extinguishing a fire after it has been brought under control.
NON-TIMBER FOREST PRODUCTS	Any commodity obtained from the forest that does not necessitate harvesting trees. Includes game animals, fur-bearers, nuts and seeds, berries, mushrooms, oils, foliage, medicinal plants, peat and fuelwood, forage, etc.
PRESCRIBED BURNING	The knowledgeable application of fire to a specific land area to accomplish predetermined forest management or other land use objectives.
SEED TREE (METHOD)	A tree left standing for the sole or primary purpose of providing seed. A method of regenerating a forest stand that involves removing all of the trees from an area in a single cut, except for a small number of seed-bearing trees. The objective is to create an even-aged stand.
SLASH BURNING	Intentional burning of debris resulting from timber harvesting operations, where the fuel has not been piled or windrowed, allowing the fire to spread freely over the entire harvested area.
SMOULDERING FIRE	A fire burning without flame and barely spreading.
SOFTWOOD	Cone-bearing tree with needles or scale-like leaves that is the predominant tree type in coniferous forests.
STAND	A continuous group of trees sufficiently uniform in age-class distribution, composition and structure, and growing on a site of sufficiently uniform quality, to be a distinguishable unit.
SUCCESSION	Changes in species composition in an ecosystem over time, often in a predictable order.
SUSTAINABLE FOREST MANAGEMENT	Management that maintains and enhances the long-term health of forest ecosystems for the benefit of all living things while providing environmental, economic, social and cultural opportunities for present and future generations.
UNDERSTOREY	The lower level of vegetation in a forest. Usually formed by ground vegetation (mosses, herbs and lichens), herbs and shrubs, but may also include subdominant trees.
UNEVEN-AGED	A stand with trees of three or more distinct age classes, either intimately mixed or in small groups.
VALUE-ADDED PRODUCT	Adding value to a product by further processing it. Examples of value-added wood products include joinery stock, windows, doors, kitchen cabinets, flooring and mouldings. Value-added pulp and paper products include such items as packaging, diapers, coated papers, tissue, business papers and stationery, and other consumer paper products.
WATER BOMBING	The act of dropping suppressants (water or short-term retardant) on a wildfire from an aircraft in flight.
WATERSHED	The area drained by an underground or surface stream, or by a system of streams.

CONTACTS

The following is a list of organizations that can provide you with additional information about Canada's forests and the forest sector.

British Columbia Market Outreach Network
1200-1130 Pender Street West
Vancouver BC V6E 4A4
Phone: (604) 685-7507/1-866-992-2266
Fax: (604) 685-5373
E-mail: info@bcmon.ca
Internet site: www.bcforestinformation.com

Canadian Federation of Woodlot Owners
180 St. John Street
Fredericton NB E3B 4A9
Phone: (506) 459-2990
Fax: (506) 459-3515
E-mail: nbfwo@nbnet.nb.ca

Canadian Forestry Association
203-185 Somerset Street West
Ottawa ON K2P 0J2
Phone: (613) 232-1815
Fax: (613) 232-4210
E-mail: cfa@canadianforestry.com
Internet site: www.canadianforestry.com

Canadian Institute of Forestry
606-151 Slater Street
Ottawa ON K1P 5H3
Phone: (613) 234-2242
Fax: (613) 234-6181
E-mail: cif@cif-ifc.org
Internet site: www.cif-ifc.org

Canadian Model Forest Network
Secretariat
Sir William Logan Building, 7th floor
580 Booth Street
Ottawa ON K1A 0E4
Phone: (613) 992-5874
Fax: (613) 992-5390
E-mail: jpugin@nrcan.gc.ca
Internet site: www.modelforest.net

Canadian Wildlife Federation
350 Michael Cowpland Drive
Kanata ON K2M 2W1
Phone: (613) 599-9594/1-800-563-WILD
Fax: (613) 599-4428
E-mail: info@cwf-fcf.org
Internet site: www.cwf-fcf.org

Council of Forest Industries
1200-Two Bentall Centre
555 Burrard Street
PO Box 276
Vancouver BC V7X 1S7
Phone: (604) 684-0211
Fax: (604) 687-4930
E-mail: info@cofi.org
Internet site: www.cofi.org

Ducks Unlimited Canada
1030 Winnipeg Street
PO Box 4465
Regina SK S4P 3W7
Phone: (306) 569-0424
Fax: (306) 565-3699
E-mail: du_regina@ducks.ca
Internet site: www.ducks.ca

Forest Engineering Research Institute of Canada (FERIC)
580, boulevard St-Jean
Pointe-Claire QC H9R 3J9
Phone: (514) 694-1140
Fax: (514) 694-4351
E-mail: admin@mtl.feric.ca
Internet site: www.feric.ca

Forest Products Association of Canada
410-99 Bank Street
Ottawa ON K1P 6B9
Phone: (613) 563-1441
Fax: (613) 563-4720
E-mail: ottawa@fpac.ca
Internet site: www.fpac.ca

Forintek Canada Corp.
2665 East Mall
Vancouver BC V6T 1W5
Phone: (604) 224-3221
Fax: (604) 222-5690
E-mail: info@van.forintek.ca
Internet site: www.forintek.ca

Gouvernement du Québec
Ministère des Ressources naturelles, de la Faune et des Parcs [Secteur des forêts]
880, chemin Ste-Foy, 10e étage
Québec QC G1S 4X4
Phone: (418) 627-8652
Fax: (418) 646-4335
E-mail: forets@mrn.gouv.qc.ca
Internet site: www.mrn.gouv.qc.ca

Government of Alberta
Ministry of Sustainable Resource Development [Public Lands and Forests Division]
Petroleum Plaza South Tower
9915-108 Street
Edmonton AB T5K 2G8
Phone: (780) 415-1396
Fax: (780) 422-6068
Internet site: www3.gov.ab.ca/srd

Government of British Columbia
Ministry of Forests [Forest Practices Branch]
727 Fisgard Street, 9th floor
PO Box 9513 Stn. Prov. Govt.
Victoria BC V8W 9C2
Phone: (250) 387-1946
Fax: (250) 387-1467
Internet site: www.gov.bc.ca/for

Government of Canada
Natural Resources Canada [Canadian Forest Service]
Sir William Logan Building, 8th floor
580 Booth Street
Ottawa ON K1A 0E4
Phone: (613) 947-7341
Fax: (613) 947-9033
E-mail: cfs-scf@nrcan.gc.ca
Internet site: www.nrcan.gc.ca/cfs-scf

Government of Manitoba
Department of Conservation [Forestry Branch]
200 Saulteaux Crescent
PO Box 70
Winnipeg MB R3J 3W3
Phone: (204) 945-7989
Fax: (204) 948-2671
E-mail: forestinfo@gov.mb.ca
Internet site: www.gov.mb.ca/conservation/forestry

Government of New Brunswick
Department of Natural Resources [Forest Management Branch]
Hugh John Flemming Forestry Centre
1350 Regent Street
PO Box 6000
Fredericton NB E3B 5H1
Phone: (506) 453-2516
Fax: (506) 453-6689
Internet site: www.gnb.ca

Government of Newfoundland and Labrador
Department of Natural Resources [Forest Resources Branch]
Natural Resources Building, 5th floor
50 Elizabeth Avenue
PO Box 8700
St. John's NL A1B 4J6
Phone: (709) 729-2704
Fax: (709) 729-3374
Internet site: www.gov.nf.ca/forestry

Government of Nova Scotia
Department of Natural Resources [Forestry Division]
Arlington Place
664 Prince Street
PO Box 68
Truro NS B2N 5B8
Phone: (902) 893-5671
Fax: (902) 893-6102
E-mail: forestry@gov.ns.ca
Internet site: www.gov.ns.ca/natr/forestry

Government of Nunavut
Department of Sustainable Development
PO Box 1000, Stn. 110
Iqaluit NU X0A 0H0
Phone: (867) 975-5925
Fax: (867) 975-5980
Internet site: www.gov.nu.ca/sd.htm

Government of Ontario
Ministry of Natural Resources [Forests Division]
Roberta Bondar Place
400-70 Foster Drive
Sault Ste Marie ON P6A 6V5
Phone: (705) 945-6746
Fax: (705) 945-5977
Internet site: www.mnr.gov.on.ca

Government of Prince Edward Island
Department of Agriculture, Fisheries, Aquaculture and Forestry [Forestry and Land Resource Modeling]
Jones Building
11 Kent Street
PO Box 2000
Charlottetown PE C1A 7N8
Phone: (902) 368-4880
Fax: (902) 368-4857
Internet site: www.gov.pe.ca/af

Government of Saskatchewan
Department of Environment
3211 Albert Street
Regina SK S4S 5W6
Phone: (306) 787-2700
Fax: (306) 787-2947
Internet site: www.se.gov.sk.ca

Government of the Northwest Territories
Department of Resources, Wildlife and Economic Development [Forest Management Division]
149 McDougal Road, 2nd floor
PO Box 7
Fort Smith NT X0E 0P0
Phone: (867) 872-7700
Fax: (867) 872-2077
Internet site: www.rwed.gov.nt.ca

Government of Yukon
Department of Energy, Mines and Resources [Forest Management Branch]
Mile 918 Alaska Highway
PO Box 2703
Whitehorse YT Y1A 2C6
Phone: (867) 667-5466
Fax: (867) 667-8601
E-mail: emr@gov.yk.ca
Internet site: www.emr.gov.yk.ca/forestry

International Model Forest Network
Secretariat
250 Albert Street, 13th floor
PO Box 8500
Ottawa ON K1G 3H9
Phone: (613) 236-6163 ext. 2521
Fax: (613) 234-7457
E-mail:imfns@idrc.ca
Internet site: www.idrc.ca/imfn

Maritime Lumber Bureau
PO Box 459
Amherst NS B4H 4A1
Phone: (902) 667-3889
Fax: (902) 667-0401
E-mail: mlb@ns.sympatico.ca
Internet site: www.mlb.ca

National Aboriginal Forestry Association
875 Bank Street
Ottawa ON K1S 3W4
Phone: (613) 233-5563
Fax: (613) 233-4329
E-mail: nafa@web.ca
Internet site: www.nafaforestry.org

National Forest Strategy Coalition
Secretariat
Sir William Logan Building, 8th floor
580 Booth Street
Ottawa ON K1A 0E4
Phone: (613) 947-9087
Fax: (613) 947-9033
E-mail: nfsc@forest.ca
Internet site: nfsc.forest.ca

National Round Table on the Environment and the Economy
200-344 Slater Street
Ottawa ON K1R 7Y3
Phone: (613) 992-7189
Fax: (613) 992-7385
E-mail: admin@nrtee-trnee.ca
Internet site: www.nrtee-trnee.ca

Pulp and Paper Research Institute of Canada (Paprican)
570, boulevard St-Jean
Pointe-Claire QC H9R 3J9
Phone: (514) 630-4100
Fax: (514) 630-4134
E-mail: info@paprican.ca
Internet site: www.paprican.ca

Quebec Forest Industry Council
1175, avenue Lavigerie, bureau 200
Sainte-Foy QC G1V 4P1
Phone: (418) 657-7916
Fax: (418) 657-7971
E-mail: info@cifq.qc.ca
Internet site: www.cifq.qc.ca

Sustainable Forest Management Network
G208 Biological Sciences Building
University of Alberta
Edmonton AB T6G 2E9
Phone: (780) 492-6659
Fax: (780) 492-8160
E-mail: sfmnweb@ualberta.ca
Internet site: sfm-1.biology.ualberta.ca

Tree Canada Foundation
1550-220 Laurier Avenue West
Ottawa ON K1P 5Z9
Phone: (613) 567-5545
Fax: (613) 567-5270
E-mail: tcf@treecanada.ca
Internet site: www.treecanada.ca

Wildlife Habitat Canada
310-1750 Courtwood Crescent
Ottawa ON K2C 2B5
Phone: (613) 722-2090
Fax: (613) 722-3318
E-mail: reception@whc.org
Internet site: www.whc.org

2005 06 20

JUN 30 2005

HUMBER COLLEGE
LIBRARY